Developing the Man

SELF-DEVELOPMENT FOR MANAGERS

A major new series of workbooks for managers edited by Jane Cranwell-Ward

This new series presents a selection of books in workbook format, on a range of key management issues and skills. The books are designed to provide practising managers with the basis for self-development across a wide range of industries and occupations.

Each book relates to other books in the series to provide a coherent new approach to self-development for managers. Closely based on the latest management training iniatives, the books are designed to complement management development programmes, in-house company training, and the management qualification programmes such as CMS, DMS, MBA and professional qualification programmes.

Other books in the series:

Thriving on Stress
Jane Cranwell-Ward

Accounting for Managers
Roger Oldcorn

Managing Change
Colin Carnall

Developing Assertiveness
Anni Townend

Effective Problem Solving
Dave Francis

The Self-reliant Manager
Chris Bones

Step-by-Step Competitive Strategy
Dave Francis

Effective Marketing
Geoffrey Randall

Improving Environmental Performance
Suzanne Pollack

The series editor, **Jane Cranwell-Ward**, is the Director of Company Programmes at Henley – The Management College. She is the author of *Managing Stress* (Pan, 1986).

Developing the Manager as a Helper

John Hayes

London and New York

First published 1996
by Routledge
11 New Fetter Lane, London EC4P 4EE

Simultaneously published in the USA and Canada
by Routledge
29 West 35th Street, New York, NY 10001

© 1996 John Hayes

Typeset in Times by Solidus (Bristol) Limited

Printed and bound in Great Britain by
Biddles Ltd, Guildford and King's Lynn

British Library Cataloguing in Publication Data
A catalogue record for this book is available from the British Library

Library of Congress Cataloging in Publication Data
Hayes, John, 1943–
    Developing the manager as a helper / John Hayes.
        p.   cm. — (Self development for managers)
    Includes bibliographical references.
    ISBN 0-415-11008-4
    1. Management. 2. Helping behavior. I. Title. I. Series.
    HD38.H3928 1995
    658.4'09—dc20   95-9517
                                          CIP

ISBN 0-415-11008-4

To Zeb and DT

Two people who have done much to help others to help themselves

— *Contents*

Figures and tables

FIGURES

TABLES

Series editor's preface

In the last decade major changes have taken place which have had considerable consequences for managers. In the 1990s organisations have been changing dramatically to face the growing competition in an international arena. These changes require managers to develop a particular set of skills to contribute to the success of their organisations.

Core functional capability is still important, but in addition managers need to develop excellent people skills. Many organisations have changed from being hierarchical and prescriptive to becoming flatter and requiring very different styles of managing.

Developing the Manager as a Helper will become a fundamental book for managers wishing to be effective in the twenty-first century. It has been developed in two parts. Part I helps the reader understand and identify his or her approach to helping others. It then goes a stage further to develop a way of helping managers to help others take responsibility for themselves. Part II clearly identifies the skills needed for helping others to help themselves. The reader is then helped to develop the skills needed for this way of working, including the important step of withdrawing once the person has solved the problem.

I was introduced to the author, John Hayes, Professor of Management Studies at the University of Leeds, by Routledge. He had previously written *Interpersonal Skills*, referred to in the text, which complements *Developing the Manager as a Helper* well. John has provided a good balance between conceptual understanding and developing the conscious behaviour needed for acquiring new skills. I am delighted to introduce this important new book to the series.

The Self Development for Managers Series has been created to help managers develop the competencies needed to be successful in this ever-changing environment. The series aims to address personal skills, functional skills, including accounting and marketing, and finally strategic skills, including competitive strategy. The complete series will give managers the level of knowledge, skill and commitment to be effective in the twenty-first century.

Jane Cranwell-Ward
Series editor

Introduction

Effective people are able to identify, appraise and where appropriate exploit opportunities. They are also able to manage problems in ways that maximise the achievement of desired outcomes and minimise the effect of dysfunctional consequences. However, some people are more effective than others. We are not all equally competent at identifying opportunities offered, for example, by a change of circumstances or at managing problems we encounter such as loss of a job or letting go of familiar work practices and adopting new ways of doing things.

This book has been written on the premise that less effective people can be helped to become more effective and that even those who are normally effective across a wide range of situations can sometimes be helped to become more effective when they encounter some novel or particularly difficult problem.

We all, to a greater or lesser extent, have the opportunity to help. Some of us work in roles that are concerned almost exclusively with helping others: for example, management consultants, social workers and AIDS counsellors. Others, such as personnel managers, systems analysts, priests and undertakers, are engaged in roles that, while not exclusively concerned with helping, involve helping as a major part of the job. However, irrespective of work role, almost everyone spends some of their time at work (and elsewhere) helping others. This might involve a colleague who requires help to improve her relationship with a major customer, a subordinate who is experiencing difficulties coping with the pressure of work, or a friend who has recently been bereaved.

Whatever our role, there are a variety of circumstances in which we might experience the need to offer help. Help might be offered informally as part of the normal day-to-day interactions we have with others. A manager might counsel a colleague who is having a difficult time with a new boss, or talk through with somebody how they will cope with working nights when their wife is admitted to hospital, leaving an infirm parent at home. Informal help might also take the form of mentoring. Experienced workers might help less experienced colleagues work out the best way of managing unfamiliar assignments. Sometimes, however, help is offered as part of a more formal interaction. In the appraisal interview, appraisers might counsel appraisees about what they could do to improve their performance, or might help them clarify career goals and identify training needs and development opportunities.

The way in which the helping process is initiated can also vary. Often the person in need of help (the client) will seek out somebody else to talk to, but self-referral is not the only starting point for a helping relationship. A manager might request or even require that one of her subordinates seeks help, for example from a member of the personnel department, the company medical officer or an external management consultant, depending on the nature of the problem. There may also be occasions when the manager is both the source of referral and the provider of help. She might have observed that a subordinate is experiencing difficulties that are threatening the success of an important project, but rather than directly intervening and transferring him to another job or taking control and telling him what to do, she might help him improve his performance by helping him develop a better understanding of the problem and working out for himself what needs to be done.

This book is intended to help managers develop helping skills. It is divided into two parts. The first three chapters provide an introduction to the nature of the helping relationship and advocate an approach to helping which involves helping others to help themselves. The second part looks at the actual skills involved.

The underlying theme of the first part of the book is that not all attempts to provide help are necessarily helpful, especially in the long run. In order to be an effective helper the manager needs to have a clear vision of what she is trying to achieve. The opening chapter invites you to complete a Helping Style Inventory in order to provide a basis for exploring your usual approach to helping. In Chapter 2 you will be encouraged to assess how effective this approach is. This relates to the underlying theme of the book that effective helping involves helping others to manage their own problems. Chapter 3 offers a six-stage model of helping that you can use to help you intervene more effectively. The six stages are:

1   Developing a helping relationship
2   Helping clients understand the problem situation
3   Helping clients set goals
4   Helping clients plan and take action
5   Consolidating the change
6   Withdrawing from the helping relationship

These stages provide a conceptual model that can be used to guide the way you relate with the person or persons you are trying to help.

Helping behaviour within each of these stages will involve a collection of different interpersonal (and intrapersonal) skills such as listening, probing for information and self-awareness. At each stage the frequency with which these skills are used and the way they are combined and sequenced will vary. For example, although listening is a vital skill that is essential at each of the six stages it forms a very major part of helper behaviour in the early stages of the helping relationship. This is in sharp contrast to the pattern and frequency with which some other skills, such as challenging and confronting, are used. Chapter 4 draws attention to those skills that can make a powerful difference to the effectiveness of the helper's attempts to help others at each stage of the helping process. These skills are:

1   Self-awareness
2   Establishing rapport and building relationships
3   Empathy
4   Listening to facts and feelings
5   Probing for information
6   Identifying themes and seeing the bigger picture
7   Giving feedback
8   Challenging assumptions

The second part of the book is concerned with developing and practising these skills. Important sub-skills (sometimes referred to as micro skills) are identified and assignments are suggested that will enable you to monitor these aspects of your behaviour and, where necessary, practise particular skills to improve the effectiveness of your helping interventions.

Part I
The Nature of Helping

1 *Helping styles*

People offer help in a variety of ways. The aim of this chapter is to help you develop a greater awareness of your normal or preferred approach to helping. Self-awareness is an important aim because it enables you to compare your usual approach with alternative approaches and offers the possibility that you might identify opportunities for modifying your style in ways that could make your interventions more effective.

The Helping Style Inventory has been designed to help you think about your usual or preferred style of helping. It will help you audit your preferred approach and provide a point of reference when thinking about how you might improve the effectiveness of your interventions. It will also help you think about whether you make appropriate use of the skills discussed in the second part of this book.

EXERCISE 1.1: HELPING STYLE INVENTORY

Listed below are five problem situations and five possible responses to each problem. You are to choose the response (from those available) which you feel you would be most likely to make. None of the available responses may provide an accurate reflection of what you would do but you are asked to circle the number of the *one* response that is most like the way you think you would respond. There are no right or wrong answers.

Situation A

A newly appointed supervisor complained to her manager that her subordinates were hostile, moody, only heard what they chose to hear and often failed to obey instructions. She likened their behaviour to rebellious schoolchildren who were determined to 'break' the new teacher. Her account placed all the blame for the rapidly deteriorating situation on to her subordinates. Her manager had not expected this kind of conversation with the new supervisor because she had joined the company with glowing references and a ten-year record of successful people management. Also, her work group had never created problems before. All of them had been with the company for at least ten months and most of them were very well qualified. Two of them had recently been through the company's assessment centre and had been identified as having potential for promotion, and another was an undergraduate on a sandwich course, working for a year in industry.

If you were the manager would you:

1   Introduce the supervisor to a theory that might help her better understand the situation. For example, the manager might explain the basics of Transactional Analysis, a theory of personal interaction which can be used to analyse interpersonal problems in terms of the intended and implied messages people send to each other. The supervisor might be asked to consider whether her subordinates see her as a controlling parent dealing with a group of inexperienced children rather than an adult interacting with other competent adults, and speculate how she might apply the theory to improve the situation by changing the way she relates with her subordinates.

2   Tell her that she has failed to recognise the quality of her subordinates, that she is undervaluing the contribution they can make, and that she needs to delegate more and give them greater responsibility.

3   Listen carefully and attempt to see the problem through her eyes in the hope that by being supportive you can encourage her to open up and tell her story, which in turn may help her to develop a better understanding of the problem and what needs to be done about it.

4   Suggest to her that it may not only be her subordinates who hear what they choose to hear and ask her if she has really paid

attention to all the messages she has been sent by the members of her work group.

5 Help her to get to the bottom of the problem by assisting her to gather more information which she can use to develop a better understanding of what is going on and what can be done to improve matters.

Situation B

One of your close friends was made redundant ten weeks ago. The news came to him as a big surprise and he was very disoriented at first. He used to 'eat, sleep and live' work and had few outside interests. However, after the initial shock, he developed a positive attitude and expressed confidence that he would soon be re-employed in the same occupation. Recently, however, you have become concerned because he seems to be giving up hope, is depressed and irritable, hardly ever leaves the house and appears to be doing little to help himself.

Would you:

1 Help him to develop a list of his strengths and weaknesses and encourage him to use this to identify some different kinds of jobs he could apply for.

2 Give him a newspaper article you came across that explained how people react to unemployment and why some are more successful at finding jobs than others, and suggest that it might give him a few ideas that would help him understand his lack of success and provide a few clues about what he might do to secure a few interviews.

3 Give him all the emotional support you can and reassure him that he is still an important and valued person.

4 Tell him to apply for a recently advertised job that you feel he could do.

5 Confront him with the confusing messages he has been giving to his friends. He is depressed and angry because he is has been deprived of the opportunity to work, and yet he is refusing to get off his backside and take the initiative to find a job simply because there do not appear to be any opportunities in his old line of work.

Situation C

You are the personnel manager of a large utility company. An employee (a 40-year-old widower) was recently promoted and moved from a busy office in the city, where he had spent most of his working life, to manage a very small but strategically important office in a relatively isolated rural area. He has come to see you because he is unhappy with the new job. He misses his friends, does not enjoy being the boss in a situation where he has no colleagues he can relate to, and he reports that people who live locally are cliquish, aloof and unfriendly.

Would you:

1   Tell him that there is a vacancy at his old grade in the department he used to work in and indicate that you think that the best solution would be for him to move back.

2   Avoid jumping to any conclusions: make sure that you really understand why he is unhappy and do everything you can to help him clarify his own feelings about what the problem might be. You might listen hard to what he has to say and then reflect back to him the essence of what you think you heard. For example, 'What you seem to be saying is ... Have I got it right?'

3   Help him adopt a balanced problem-solving approach and encourage him to explore thoroughly every aspect of the problem and, where necessary, gather information that might help him identify and evaluate possible solutions (for example, by helping him identify opportunities to meet new people).

4   Give him the kind of feedback that might push him into taking a new initiative, for example by telling him that you have listened to what he has said and not once heard him mention anything that he has actually done to try to make new friends. All he seems to do is moan about others and complain that they do nothing to make him welcome. You might try to encourage him into action by asking him if he has thought about what he might do that would make others want to get to know him better.

5   Lend him a copy of Dale Carnegie's book *How to Win Friends and Influence People* and suggest that if he could master some of the techniques and skills it contains then making friends might be something which he could do more easily.

Situation D

You are the general manager of a large manufacturing plant and are in the middle of an appraisal interview with one of your departmental managers. You used to regard her as one of your 'rising stars' but you have been disappointed with her performance of late. You put her in charge of a task force that was established to conduct a wide-ranging review of the company's manufacturing strategy and you suspect she will not deliver the report on time. You are also concerned that she is involved with too many staff association and other activities that, in your opinion, do little to contribute to the 'bottom line'.

At an early point in the interview she tells you that she has been looking forward to this meeting because she feels overworked and was hoping that you might be able to help. She explains that she believes her subordinates would be unhappy if she tried to delegate more work to them. She also doubts their ability to take on any more of her work.

Would you:

1   Tell her that you are aware of the problem and that you think the first thing she must do is to sort out her priorities and drop all the non-important tasks that are eating into her time.
2   Suggest that the company's seminars on Time Management and Delegation might help her identify constructive methods of shifting some of her work to others in ways that they will welcome and see as contributing to their own personal development.
3   Explore how she feels about the situation without passing judgement or telling her what she should do. Encourage her to talk about it and gently encourage her to examine any aspects of the problem she seems to have skirted over so that she is able to develop a more balanced view.
4   Suggest that it might be useful to find out how the members of her department feel about their work and the way the department is operating, and offer her a copy of an attitude survey form that she might be able to adapt and use.
5   Make her face up to reality and recognise that she is not the only competent person around. You might ask if she really thinks she is indispensable and suggest that some of her subordinates might be able to do some things better than her if she would only let go of the reins and gave them a chance.

Situation E

A colleague has come to you for help. He does not want to be an autocratic boss and believes that people work best when they are given the freedom to get on with their job. However, his department is beginning to get itself a reputation for not getting it right. He has explained that, while he always tries to pursue an open-door policy, there are some people who never cross his threshold. Consequently he is badly informed and avoidable mistakes have been made. He is obviously upset and you suspect that his boss has just had him in and torn a strip off him.

Would you:

1   Share with him a similar problem you once had and tell him what you did about it. Also suggest that there can come a time when democracy has to go out of the window and you have to read the riot act. And that's what he should do now.

2   Tell him about a theory you are familiar with that argues that the best style of leadership might vary from one situation to another, and suggest that one way forward might be for him to consider whether his current style appears to be a 'best fit' or whether the theory would suggest an alternative leadership style.

3   On the basis of what you have observed (and been told by others), challenge his view that he always operates an open-door policy. Tell him that you have heard that he is never around when he is needed. Also that while he might believe he is approachable others see him as aloof and distant.

4   You can see that he is upset so decide that the best thing you can do is to sit him down with a cup of coffee and let him get it off his chest.

5   Help him identify some specific circumstances where things have gone wrong and then question him about a number of these problems to sort out precisely what happened and whether there are any recurring patterns that he could do something about.

Scoring

In the grid below, the situations (A to E) are listed down the left-hand side and the responses (1 to 5) fall into the five categories of helping style (Theorising, Advising, Supporting, Challenging and Information Gathering) which are listed along the top. Look at the response you have selected for each situation and circle the corresponding number on the appropriate row. For example, if you chose response 3 to situation A then circle the 3 on the first row. Do this for all five situations and then add up how many numbers you have circled in each column.

Helping style

Response	Theorising	Advising	Supporting	Challenging	Information gathering
A	1	2	3	4	5
B	2	4	3	5	1
C	5	1	2	4	3
D	2	1	3	5	4
E	2	1	4	3	5
Totals					

You should now have a score for all five types of helping style. Note whether your scores were equally spread across all five helping styles or whether you produced a response pattern that was clustered around a few styles, or even just one style.

DIFFERENT APPROACHES TO HELPING

The five approaches to helping presented in the Helping Style Inventory represent some of the ways in which people attempt to help others. This section will discuss each of these approaches in turn and the following section will consider the implications of different kinds of response to the Helping Style Inventory.

Theorising

This is an approach to helping which involves the helper identifying theories, concepts and principles which are relevant to the client's problem, presenting them to the client and helping him to use them to develop an understanding of his problem in an analytical, cause-and-effect fashion. The aim of this approach to helping is to encourage the client to use this understanding to identify ways in which desired changes can be secured.

A manager might adopt a theorising approach when she feels that some kind of theoretical framework could help a colleague organise his thoughts and provide the basis for a fresh appraisal of his predicament. For example, the colleague might be a production superintendent who is in trouble because the people working for him are failing to deliver the required level of output. He might be at his wits' end because he feels that he has tried everything, including managing by walking about in order to keep a close eye on what is going on, disciplining those who he finds are failing to pull their weight, and introducing a piece rate scheme to provide an incentive for people to work harder.

The manager/helper could approach this problem by inviting the production superintendent to consider why he has taken the action he has (in other words, by trying to help him raise his awareness of, and make more explicit, his implicit theory of motivation and his assumptions about what factors influence how hard people work), and then introducing him to an alternative theory that might provide a more effective framework for diagnosing problem situations and planning appropriate remedial action. In this example the helper might use this approach to help the production superintendent recognise that all his previous attempts to solve the problem seem to have been based upon the assumptions that form the basis for McGregor's Theory X (see his book *The Human Side of Enterprise*), i.e. that the average person has an inherent dislike of work, will avoid it if he can and therefore must be coerced, controlled, directed and threatened with punishment in order to get him to work harder. The helper might contrast this with McGregor's Theory Y, which assumes that external control and the threat of punishment are not the only means of motivating others. It suggests that people will exercise self-direction and self-control in the service of objectives to which they are committed, and that this commitment is associated with the rewards associated with the achievement of those objectives. This theoretical perspective might encourage the production superintendent to give fresh thought to what it is that motivates his subordinates and consider whether it is the design of the work they are given to do that could be the cause of their lack of effort. He might be persuaded to use this new theoretical framework to guide his attempts to improve matters and he might, for example, decide to consider whether the work could be redesigned to make the operatives' jobs more meaningful, give them more responsibility for outcomes and provide them with feedback about how well they are doing.

This theory-based approach has a number of advantages. It can facilitate discussion and open the way to an exploration of potentially delicate or sensitive issues, it can provide a way of exploring and testing implicit assumptions and values that avoids direct confrontation, and it also provides a basis for increasing the client's capacity for independent action.

Advising

The advising approach involves the helper giving advice and telling the client what to do. Often the advice offered is based upon the helper's own direct or indirect experience and involves either the recommendation of action that she believes will work, or a warning to avoid behaving in ways that she believes will fail to deliver desired outcomes. People tend to adopt this approach when they believe that they have a greater level of relevant expertise than the client. Consequently they feel qualified to diagnose the client's problem and prescribe what he needs to do to improve matters. Sometimes, especially when the client is slow to act, the 'advising' helper might even intervene and take some direct action which she feels will be in the client's best interest. For example, a well-intentioned helper might write off for a number of job application forms for her partner because she knows that he is unhappy at work. This approach assumes that the helper knows what is best for the client.

One danger with this approach is that the client becomes dependent on the helper. He is not helped to learn how to solve problems for himself. He is given a solution. Consequently the next time he encounters a problem he has to turn to others for advice.

Another problem can arise when the client feels that the helper is not as expert as she thinks she is, or if he feels that she is insensitive to his needs. He may react by not co-operating with the helper and withholding information about the problem. He may also reject the advice or solution offered. However, some clients do respond well to advice offered by prescriptive helpers, especially when they are under great pressure to find a solution. Indeed, some clients may actively seek advice and become frustrated with helpers who are either unwilling or unable to provide it as and when required. In such circumstances great care needs to be taken to ensure that the client is not encouraged to become too dependent on the helper. This point is developed later.

Supporting

The supporting approach is based upon the Rogerian client-centred counselling model in which the counsellor listens, reflects and sometimes interprets what the client has said about himself and his relationship with others, but does not intervene or develop any active strategies for dealing with the client's problem. In this respect the supporting approach is completely different from the advising approach. The focus of the interaction is the client, not the problem. Supportive interventions involve the helper working with the client to help him express those feelings and emotions which impede clear and objective thinking about a problem. The helper listens empathically, withholding judgement, and helps the client develop for himself a more objective view of the situation. It is sometimes assumed that this new level of awareness will be sufficient to help the client go on to solve the problem for himself.

Blake and Mouton, in their book *Consultation*, describe a supporting intervention that took place between a consultant and a shop floor worker in the Hawthorne plant of Western Electric. The consultant overheard the worker complaining, in very emotional tones, about his supervisor and decided to intervene. He asked what had been going on and was told, in the same emotional tones, that the bosses were not worth a damn because 'when you have a rise coming to you they will not give it'. He went on to tell the consultant that he thought 'the place stinks' and that he wanted to get out. The consultant's response was to avoid siding with either the worker or the supervisor, but to invite the worker into his office to 'talk it over till quitting time'.

Once they were in the office the worker continued as before and the consultant listened while he unloaded his feelings about his supervisor. As he went on he began to ramble from one complaint to another. Not only had he been refused a rise but, because he was the top of grade 34, he could not advance any higher. He then complained about the machine setters, who did everything they could to stop others learning anything. All the way through this interaction the consultant maintained his neutral stance and refrained from any evaluation of the worker's complaints. He had been actively listening but did little more than reflect his sympathetic understanding by repeating what he had been told. For example, in response to the complaint about the machine setters, he said, 'I see, they seem to be pretty selfish about their knowledge of screw machines.'

The consultant's strategy was to allow the worker to vent his anger because he believed that until he had done this the worker would be too wound up to think straight. This strategy appeared to work. Slowly, as the tension eased, the conversation moved away from gripes towards problem solving, even though the consultant confined his interventions to supportive listening and clarifying.

Challenging

This is an approach which involves the helper confronting the foundations of the client's thinking in an attempt to identify assumptions and values which may be distorting the way situations are viewed. Sometimes effective action is undermined by the client's inability or unwillingness to face up to reality. He may rationalise or justify his behaviour and in so doing create or perpetuate an unsatisfactory situation. Challenging interventions are designed to call attention to contradictions in action and attitude or challenge precedents or practices which seem inappropriate. The objective is to identify alternative values and assumptions that might lead to the development of more effective solutions to problems. For example, a head teacher of a small school who had worked tremendously hard to improve the school's external reputation and had invested a great deal of effort in building a good team spirit among his staff had interpreted one member of staff's application for a new job elsewhere as a sign of disloyalty. He responded by communicating this to the individual concerned and making his disapproval public by excluding him from management team meetings. The deputy head intervened by confronting the head with his own career progression. He pointed out that the head had rarely stayed in one job for more than three years whereas this individual had already been in post and had performed very satisfactorily for almost four years. He also asked him how he thought others would interpret his action and what effect it was likely to have on the team spirit he prized so highly. Eventually the head accepted that the teacher's application was a timely and appropriate step to take and that he not only had overlooked the career development needs of this individual but had given insufficient attention to the career development of all of his staff. He also accepted that his response had been inconsistent with the management culture he was trying to create.

Egan, in *The Skilled Helper*, argues that confrontation can be strong medicine and, in the hands of the inept, can be destructive. Challenges that are perceived as punitive accusations or the shameful unmasking of inadequacies are likely to be met with some form of strong defensive reaction. Effective challenges are those which are received as helpful invitations to explore aspects of a problem from a new perspective. Helpers adopting this approach ask questions or provide feedback that draws the client's attention to inappropriate attitudes, values, discrepancies and distortions, but they avoid telling the client how he should think or act.

Information gathering

This approach to helping involves the helper assisting the client collect data which can be used to evaluate and reinterpret the problem situation. For example, a trainer in the sales department of a machine tool company suggested to a young representative, who was very de-motivated after losing three accounts in as many weeks, that he get in touch with the buyers he used to deal with and ask them why they had changed suppliers. The trainer suspected that it was because the rep had not been attentive enough but he felt that it would be more effective if the rep discovered this and decided for himself what he needed to do about it.

Helpers adopting this approach assume that deficiencies of information are an important cause of malfunctioning and their objectives are to help the client arrive at a better level of awareness of the underlying causes of a problem and to help him identify what action is required to resolve it. The helpers assume that information which individuals (or groups) generate for themselves is understood better and is more acceptable than that which is presented by outsiders. Another assumption often made by helpers adopting this approach is that clients will be less resistant to proposals that they have generated for themselves. Consequently they tend to ensure that clients participate fully in the analysis and interpretation of the information when it is available.

There may be occasions when the client is too busy or for some other reason is unable to gather the information, or when he feels that an outsider may be able to collect more objective data than he could. However, in such circumstances the helper will strive to ensure that the client retains control. For example, the chairman of a construction company was concerned about the high level of hostility and conflict in board meetings and approached a consultant for help. She suggested that she should interview, individually, every director about how well they felt the board was performing and what could be done to make it more effective. When the consultant presented the results of her survey to the chairman he was not surprised to discover that most of the directors felt that the board was failing to meet its objectives, but he was amazed to discover that there was no agreement about what those objectives were. He discussed these findings with the consultant and decided to call a special meeting to thrash out what the board's objectives should be. Once there was agreement on this, directors were able to work together much more effectively because they had a common purpose.

It has been suggested that a major weakness with this approach is that it may ignore the possibility that information deficiency could be a symptom, rather than the cause, of the problem. Consequently the helper may focus her attention on making the information available and fail to help the client consider why it was not available in the first place.

IS THERE ONE BEST APPROACH?

Many people use a variety of helping styles, depending on their perception of the needs of the client and the nature of the problem, and this is reflected in the way they respond to the Helping Style Inventory. They may select responses that are drawn from three, four or even all five of the helping styles. Others, however, use the same approach in most of the cases presented in the Inventory. It may be that many of those who respond in this way make use of all five approaches in different circumstances but feel that, on reading the particular cases presented in the Inventory, one approach is best for most of them. On the other hand it is possible that they have a predisposition to respond in the same way in most circumstances. The danger with such a predisposition is that the helper's behaviour may not be related to the client's needs. However, in some cases there may be a happy coincidence between the helper's predisposition and the client's needs. For example, it may be that in those circumstances where emotions and pent-up feelings are getting in the way of the client's ability to stand back and view the situation objectively, as in the case of the angry worker mentioned above, a supporting approach will be much more effective than a theorising approach. This may be because until the client has vented his feelings it might be difficult for him to think straight and adopt a constructive approach to solving his problem. However, if the helper over-relies on this supporting approach, even in situations where there may be a need to confront an apparent discrepancy between what the client wants and the way he is behaving, or the standards he uses to guide his own behaviour and those he uses to judge others (as in the case of the head teacher), the assistance provided may not be very helpful.

Similarly, an over-reliance on one approach to helping at all stages of the helping process may undermine the effectiveness of the help offered. For example, in the angry worker case the helper may find that once the client has discharged his pent-up feelings he may begin to accept his predicament and lose the desire to deal with the problem. In such circumstances continued use of the supportive approach may not be what is required.

If there is a best approach it must be one that matches the helper's behaviour with the client's needs, and since these needs may change at different stages of the helping process then so the best approach may also change. A supporting approach may help a client calm down and free himself of highly charged emotions that distort his perception of the problem, but thereafter he may require help to overcome a communication problem that restricts access to important information (information gathering) or benefit from a theory-based intervention that provides a conceptual framework to guide his exploration of the problem or help him develop an action plan that takes account of, for example, how others are likely to respond to different kinds of initiative.

Chapter 3 will develop these ideas within the context of an integrated approach to problem management and Chapter 4 will provide an introduction to a range of helping skills.

ESPOUSED THEORIES AND THEORIES IN USE

Your response to the Helping Style Inventory may not provide an accurate reflection of how you actually behave in practice. It may reflect the way you think a helper should behave and therefore the way you would like to think you behave. Chris Argyris, in an article in *Organizational Dynamics*, argues that people acquire, through socialisation, two kinds of skills and values for dealing with people. The first are the values and skills they espouse, the ones they are conscious and aware of. He refers to these as an individual's *espoused theories of action*. Your response to the Helping Style Inventory might be a reflection of your espoused theory of action and this may be inconsistent with how you actually behave when faced with the need to help somebody with a difficult problem. Your actual behaviour is a reflection of what Argyris refers to as your *theory in use*. We are rarely aware of our theory in use because it is ingrained in us from early childhood. It is the effect of social conditioning and is something that we do not normally think about.

Covey, in *The Seven Habits of Highly Effective People*, suggests that we are a product of our habits. He argues that habits are powerful factors in determining how effective we are because they are both consistent and unconscious. Blake and Mouton, in their book *Consultation*, also refer to the cyclical nature of behaviour and note that it can become so habitual as to be beyond the conscious control of the person, group, organisation or community whose performance it characterises. Habitual behaviour is not necessarily ineffective behaviour, but because we may not be aware of our habitual predisposition to behave in the way we do, we may be unaware of the potential for improvement.

The Helping Style Inventory is designed to help you identify your espoused theory of helping, whereas the next two exercises are designed to raise your awareness of your theory of helping in use, and to provide you with the opportunity to assess how consistent this is with your espoused theory.

EXERCISE 1.2: YOUR THEORY OF HELPING IN USE

The aim of this exercise is to help you identify similarities and differences between the way you responded to the Helping Style Inventory and your recollections of how you actually behaved when helping others.

Think of two occasions when you have offered help to another person. If possible, select two helping episodes that were as different as possible. For example, one might have involved helping a loved one faced with a relationship problem (such as a son or daughter who has been let down by a partner, or a close friend or a parent who has been bereaved), and the other might have involved helping a colleague or subordinate with a work-related problem (such as coping with a demanding new boss or dealing with an unreliable but irreplaceable supplier).

In the space provided write a short account of what happened. Try to recall how you became aware of the need to offer help, what you felt like at the time and what you did to help. (These accounts will also be used as the basis for exercises in Chapters 2 and 3.)

First case:

Second case:

Refresh your memory of the five helping styles presented earlier in this chapter and consider whether it is possible to classify the approach you adopted in each of your two cases in terms of these styles. Some people find that it is fairly easy to identify one underlying approach, such as challenging or advising, whereas others see their approach as more complex, involving a combination of styles, such as supporting followed by information gathering.

Were the approaches that you adopted in these two cases similar to those you adopted when responding to the Helping Style Inventory? Although the structure of the Helping Style Inventory restricts your freedom to respond and forces you to choose one response to each situation, it is still possible to use your aggregate response to the five situations as a basis for assessing the degree of congruence which exists between your espoused theory and your theory in use.

SELF-AWARENESS: AN ESSENTIAL FOUNDATION

If your responses to the two exercises were significantly different this may signal that you need to work at improving your level of self-awareness. In order to become a more effective helper you need to be aware of how you actually behave in practice and to be sensitive to feedback so that you are able to assess the efficacy of your current approach.

When you have a high level of self-awareness you are able to compare the approach you use in practice with alternatives, such as the integrated model of helping presented in Chapter 3, and identify aspects of your existing approach which you may wish to change. If, however, you are out of touch with your theory in use, and if your theory in use is significantly different from your espoused theory of helping, then you may fail to recognise opportunities for improvement. Further attention will be given to the issue of helper self-awareness in Chapter 5.

2 Helping others to help themselves

This chapter considers whether help is always helpful, argues that effective help involves helping others to help themselves, and introduces an exercise designed to enable you to assess how helpful your preferred approach to helping is.

Often, ineffective people are ineffective because they fail to think or act in ways that enable them to exercise the control necessary to achieve desired outcomes. Rollo May argues that many people are hypnotised by their own feelings of powerlessness and use this as an excuse for doing nothing. He describes the central core of modern man's neuroses as the undermining of his experience of himself as responsible, and the sapping of his will and ability to make decisions. According to May, in *Love and Will*,

> the lack of will is much more than merely an ethical problem: the modern individual so often has the conviction that even if he did exert his 'will' – or whatever illusion passes for it – his actions wouldn't do any good anyway.

This inner feeling of impotence is a critical problem for some people, and undermines their ability to manage their lives effectively.

The reason why many people become clients in need of help is that they lack confidence in their own ability to help themselves. If the helper responds by providing the client with an immediate solution this may reinforce the client's belief in his own inability to manage his own affairs and have the effect of making him *more*, rather than less, dependent on others. In other words, not all help is necessarily helpful. The underlying theme of this book is that the most effective help is that which promotes self-efficacy and helps others to help themselves.

SOME USEFUL THEORETICAL CONTRIBUTIONS

After observing that some of their clients seemed to attribute outcomes to luck rather than to factors over which they had some control, two psychologists, Rotter and Phares, embarked on a programme of research which led to the development of the concept of the 'locus of control'. The locus of control reflects the degree to which people believe that their own behaviour determines what happens to them. Those who attribute outcomes to their own efforts are referred to as internals and those who attribute outcomes to external factors such as luck, fate, other people, the state of the economy or other factors over which they have no control are referred to as externals.

In recent years a variety of measures of the locus of control have been developed but most adopt the format that was originally used by Rotter in which respondents are presented with a number of forced-choice items and asked to choose the statement in each pair of alternatives which they *believe* to be true. The following examples are similar to some of the items included in the original scales. Read through them and note your own response.

(a) Many of the unhappy things in people's lives are partly due to bad luck.
(b) People's misfortunes result from their own mistakes.

(a) There is not much you can do to affect whether people will like you.
(b) People are lonely because they do not try to be friendly to others.

(a) Marriage is largely a gamble.
(b) The growing number of divorces indicates that more and more people are failing to work at making their marriage a success.

(a) I have little influence over the way people behave.
(b) If one knows how to deal with people it is relatively easy to influence them.

(a) Unfortunately, an individual's worth often passes unrecognised no matter how hard she tries.
(b) In the long run people get the respect they deserve.

In the examples presented above all the (a) items reflect an external and the (b) items reflect an internal locus of control.

People with a high external score are less likely to see any connection between either their effort or ability and the achievement of desirable outcomes. Consequently, if externals are successful they are less likely than internals to learn from their success and identify things which *they* could do to exercise more control over outcomes. Internals, on the other hand, are more likely to attribute success or failure to their own effort or ability, to learn from their experience and to take more responsibility for solving their own problems. However, those with a high internal score who always attribute success or failure to themselves may, in circumstances where the situation is such that whatever they do they are unlikely to be able to influence outcomes, experience dysfunctional effects such as a steady erosion of self-esteem. Seligman's work, reported below, sheds more light on these dysfunctional effects and develops an interesting theory concerning control processes.

Learned helplessness

Seligman, in *Helplessness*, presents a theory of learned helplessness which argues that people's expectations about their ability to control outcomes is influenced by their experience.

The theory states that when individuals are subjected to events which are uncontrollable (that is, when the probability of an outcome is the same irrespective of how hard they work to influence what happens) they will develop the *expectation* that whatever they do they will not be able to exercise much influence over outcomes. This expectation will produce what Seligman referred to as motivational and cognitive deficits.

The motivational deficits involve a *failure to take any voluntary actions designed to control events* following a previous experience with uncontrollable events. Because the individual believes that he cannot exercise any control over outcomes he is not motivated even to try. The experimental evidence shows that subjects become passive when they experience uncontrollable events and that this passivity continues over successive trials. Francis, in *Effective Problem*

Solving, an earlier book in this series, argues that capable problem solvers are strongly motivated to defeat any difficulties. They are energised rather than weakened by problems and redouble their commitment when things go wrong. They make realistic assessments about their ability to control outcomes and are not easily de-motivated by early failures. They are persistent. Ineffective problem solvers often lack this motivation because they do not have any confidence in their own ability to succeed.

The cognitive deficits involve a *failure to learn* that it is possible to control what happens. Once people have learned that they are helpless they may fail to recognise opportunities to exercise influence even after their own behaviour has had an important impact on outcomes.

Implications for the helper

Seligman's theory suggests that the incentive for the client to initiate activity directed towards resolving a problem depends upon the expectation that his action will produce some improvement in the problem situation. If the client does not have any confidence in his own ability to achieve any improvements he will not try. A distinction that Seligman and others make between universal helplessness (where the client believes that the problem is unsolvable by anyone) and personal helplessness (where the client believes the problem is solvable – for example, by the helper – but not by him) provides some indication of the kind of help that will and will not be helpful. In particular, this distinction highlights the danger of prescriptive approaches to helping, which can have the effect of promoting a sense of *personal helplessness*. Telling the client what to do may reinforce his belief that he is unable to control outcomes and must rely on others for help.

In those situations where a client has no confidence in his own ability to control outcomes, helpful help needs to be directed towards reversing the expectation that acting to improve a situation will be a waste of time and effort. The client will not be motivated to help himself so long as he expects that his attempts to control a situation will have no impact on the eventual outcome. Changing this expectation will involve changing the client's attribution for success or failure to factors that he can do something about.

HELPING CLIENTS MANAGE THEIR OWN PROBLEMS MORE EFFECTIVELY

Egan, in *The Skilled Helper*, discusses the notion of empowerment in the helping relationship. He notes that some clients learn, sometimes from a very early age, that there is nothing they can do about certain life situations. They engage in disabling self-talk and tell themselves that they cannot manage these kinds of situation and that they cannot cope. Egan's position is that whether clients are victims because of their own doing or because of the doings of others they can and must take an active part in managing their own problems, including the search for solutions and efforts towards achieving those solutions. Helpers can help their clients challenge self-defeating beliefs and attitudes about themselves and can help them develop more realistic beliefs regarding their ability to control outcomes. They can also help their clients develop the knowledge, skills and resources they need to succeed, and they can encourage them to take reasonable risks and support them when they do.

Effective helping involves helping others to help themselves. This involves helping clients reappraise their attributions for success and failure and helping them improve their own ability to exercise control over outcomes. There may be situations where the client has correctly attributed to his own actions a failure to secure a desired outcome, but has not fully appreciated the possibilities open to him for changing the way he acts so as to exercise more control over outcomes. The helper might assist the client recognise that he could act more effectively if he could develop new skills. This may take some time. None the less, while the client may not be able to secure an instant improvement he can be helped to begin to accept more responsibility for the achievement of desired outcomes.

There may also be some circumstances where, after a thorough exploration of the problem, the client has to accept that there is little he can do to control events, but even in these situations he can be helped to manage the way he responds to such circumstances. For example, other people cannot make the client angry; he can *choose* to make himself angry in response to what these other people do. We can all learn to make the best of those situations that we cannot change and learn to cope in ways that minimise undesirable consequences for ourselves and others. We may not be able to escape the consequences of a terminal illness but we can manage our own response to the circumstances in which we find ourselves.

There are many similarities in the helping philosophies that are central to the Organisation Development approach to improving organisational effectiveness and the personal empowerment approach to improving individual effectiveness which is advocated here. Central to both is a similar conception regarding the role of the helper, or change agent. It involves encouraging the client or client system to apply a problem-solving approach to the current problem situation and, while learning how to manage this current problem more effectively, learn transferable problem management skills that they will be able to apply to any new problems they may encounter.

While providing the client with solutions might improve his predicament in the short term it will do little to improve his ability to manage problems and exploit opportunities in the longer term. It will do little to make him a more effective person and may serve to make him more passive and dependent on others. The distinction between proaction and reaction was first made more than thirty years ago by G.W. Allport when he defined proaction as acting on the environment. Encouraging proactivity is an important goal. The aim of the helping relationship is to encourage and assist others to become more proactive in the management of their own problems. It involves empowering them to act on their own behalf.

The next exercise has been designed to help you develop a little more awareness of your approach to helping. It relates to some of the ideas that have already been discussed and it also relates to some of the ideas that will be presented in the next chapter.

EXERCISE 2.1: WHY AND WHAT

Return to the two cases that you used in Exercise 1.2 (pages 23–4) and answer the following questions.

Case 1
Why did you intervene?

How did you intervene – what did you actually do in order to help the other person?

Were you clear about how the action you took would help the client (i.e. was it designed to achieve a specific change?). If yes, specify:

Did you consider the possibility of providing the help in some other way? If yes, why did you decide to do what you did rather than provide the help in some other way?

Case 2
Why did you intervene?

How did you intervene – what did you actually do in order to help the other person?

Were you clear about how the action you took would help the client (i.e. was it designed to achieve a specific change?). If yes, specify:

Did you consider the possibility of providing the help in some other way? If yes, why did you decide to do what you did rather than provide the help in some other way?

Reflect on your answer to the first question in Exercise 2.1 and consider your *motivation* for helping. Was your prime motive to help the other person (the client), or to satisfy some personal need of your own? Sometimes helpers intervene because they are disturbed by the other person's distress (and possibly tears) and want to remove the source of their own discomfort by providing the client with a quick-fix solution. In this kind of situation the helper's prime aim is not to help the client but to help herself.

Now reflect on your answers to the remaining questions. Before you took any action had you thought about what you wanted to achieve for the client and about what you could do to secure this outcome? Helpers can be more effective when they are clear about *what* they want to achieve and *how* they can best achieve it.

Chapter 2 has discussed the aims of helping and has argued that effective help involves helping others to help themselves. Chapter 3 will present a conceptual map that can help the helper intervene more effectively.

3   A six-stage model for helping

In the previous chapter we discussed helping in terms of helping others to help themselves. This chapter will look at how that philosophy can be applied in practice and will provide a conceptual map to guide both helper and client through the helping process.

If helping is defined in terms of assisting others to become more proactive in the management of their own problems then the helper needs to understand the nature of problems and to have a clear view of how an outsider (a helper) can help another person (the client) learn how to manage problems more effectively.

THE NATURE OF PROBLEMS

Jackson argues that an essential first step in problem management is problem definition. In his book *The Art of Problem Solving*, he suggests that all problems have two outstanding features: an objective that someone is trying to achieve, and an obstacle that is preventing him or her from achieving it. While this definition, which can be expressed in terms of a simple mnemonic $P = O + O$ (where P is the problem and one O is the objective and the other O the obstacle), can be very useful it can also be limiting in so far as it may encourage people to define problems in terms of things going wrong. A problem exists when something is not working the way it should, therefore it needs 'fixing'. This approach implies that if everything is working normally there is no problem and no action is required. 'If it isn't broken, don't fix it.'

Edward de Bono suggests, in his book *I Am Right – You Are Wrong*, that this maintenance approach to the definition of problems and problem management excludes opportunity thinking, initiative taking, enterprise, improvement and all those types of thinking in which people set out to think about things which are not wrong. It excludes the notion of progress through changes in perceptions, paradigm shifts and deliberate design. Egan offers a definition which avoids this difficulty. In *The Skilled Helper* he defines problems in terms of *problem situations* where the client is experiencing crises, troubles, doubts, difficulties, frustrations or concerns, and *missed opportunities and unused potential*. Here the focus is not restricted to what is going wrong, but also includes what could be done better and the client's failure to take advantage of opportunities or under-used potential.

EXERCISE 3.1: STAGES IN THE HELPING PROCESS

Before reading on, refer to your answers to Exercise 2.1 (on pages 23–4) where you thought about why you intervened and what it was that you hoped to achieve by helping. Consider whether it is useful to think of the helping process in terms of a series of stages. If so, what are the main stages and what is the aim of each stage? Do they have a natural sequence?

In the space below, list what you believe are the main steps in the helping process, and if you feel they follow a natural sequence list them in order:

THE HELPING PROCESS

Lewin provided some useful insights into the nature of change that are relevant to the helping process. In an article published in *Human Relations* he argued that the state of no change does not refer to a situation in which everything is stationary. It involves a condition of 'stable quasi-stationary equilibrium' comparable to that of a river which flows with a given velocity in a given direction during a certain time interval. A change in an individual's or a group's behaviour can be likened to a change in the river's velocity or direction. In a work situation, for example, certain hostile and friendly actions may occur between two groups in an interdepartmental meeting. If the level of hostile behaviour is defined as a problem, a desired change may involve a reduction in hostile behaviour and an increase in friendly behaviour, in other words in a move from one state of stable quasi-stationary equilibrium to another.

Lewin argued that any level of behaviour is maintained in a condition of quasi-stationary equilibrium by a force field comprising a balance of forces pushing for and resisting change. This level of behaviour can be changed either by adding forces for change in the desired direction or by diminishing the opposing or resisting forces. Both of these approaches can result in change but, according to Lewin, the secondary effects associated with each approach will be different. Where change is brought about by increasing the forces pushing for change this will result in an increase in tension, and if this rises beyond a certain level it may be accompanied by higher levels of aggressiveness (especially towards the source of the increased pressure for change), higher levels of emotionality and lower constructiveness. On the other hand, where change is brought about by diminishing the forces which oppose or resist change the secondary effect will be a state of relatively low tension. This argument led Lewin to advocate the latter approach (diminishing restraining forces) in preference to the high-pressure approach (increasing the forces pushing for change). He also argued that approaches which involve the removal of restraining forces within the individual or group will result in a more permanent change than high-pressure approaches which involve the application of outside pressure.

ACHIEVING A LASTING CHANGE

This concept of permanency is important. Lewin suggested that successful change requires a three-step procedure involving the stages of unfreezing, moving and refreezing. He argued that all too often change is short-lived. After a 'shot in the arm' life returns to the way it was before. It is not enough to think of change in terms of simply *reaching* a new state, for example a new pattern of behaviour towards subordinates. Permanency, at least for a desired period, needs to be an important part of the goal. Helping somebody, therefore, involves helping them unfreeze or unlock from the existing level of behaviour, move to a new level and refreeze their behaviour at this new level.

THE STAGES OF THE HELPING PROCESS

Lippitt, Watson and Westley, in *The Dynamics of Planned Change*, expanded this three-stage model. After reviewing descriptions of change in persons, groups, organisations and communities they felt that the moving phase divided naturally into three sub-stages. These were:

1   The clarification or diagnosis of the client's problem
2   The examination of alternative routes and goals – establishing goals and intentions for action
3   The transformation of intentions into actual change efforts

They also argued that helpers can be effective only when they develop and maintain an appropriate relationship with their clients. This led them to introduce two further stages into the helping process: one concerned with the formation and the other with the termination of relationships.

Lippitt, Watson and Westley's elaboration of Lewin's three-stage model provides a framework that embraces many popular models of helping and problem solving. This is illustrated in Table 3.1.

Do any of these stage models resemble the stages you identified in your answer to Exercise 3.1?

Table 3.1 Models of the helping process

	Unfreezing	Moving	Refreezing
Lewin			
Lippitt et al.	Developing a need for change / Establishing a need for a change	Clarification of the problem / Examination of alternatives and the establishment of goals and intentions for action / Transformation of intentions into actual change efforts	Generalisation and stabilisation of change / Achieving a terminal relationship
Jackson	Formulating / –	Interpreting / Constructing courses of action / Decision making / Implementation	– / –
Francis		←— Tuning in —→ Objective setting / Success measures / Information collection / Decision making / Planning / Action	Review / –
Egan	Identifying and clarifying problem situations and unused opportunties	Developing a preferred scenario / Formulating strategies and plans	? / Termination

HOW A MODEL CAN HELP

Many people have a very limited view of helping. They may, for example, think of it only in terms of empathic listening or the provision of feedback. This may be because they lack an overview of the process and tend to concentrate their efforts on only one aspect of the helping relationship. For example, the supportive model of helping (one of the five approaches discussed in Chapter 1) focuses on the provision of empathy and passive support aimed at helping clients develop a new level of understanding of their problems. Some helpers may assume that this new understanding will enable clients to move forward, without further help, and manage their problems more effectively for themselves. While this might be the case for some clients there will be others who will not know what to do with this new awareness; they will require further help to establish realistic goals and develop action plans.

Many helpers tend to develop one style of intervention and rely on it exclusively. However, as mentioned in Chapter 1, over-reliance on one style of helping at every stage in the helping process may seriously undermine the effectiveness of the help offered. For example, the helper who specialises in challenging may not be very good at this unless her challenges are based on an empathic understanding of the client and his problems.

Conceptual models provide an overview of the helping process and provide the helper with an agenda of issues that need to be attended to. They can also assist helpers understand the nature of their relationship with clients, provide a cognitive map that can help them diagnose what kind of help each client needs, and provide them with a sense of direction. Although most models involve a series of stages this does not necessarily imply that the helping process progresses in an orderly way through these stages. The helper may move backwards as well as forwards through the model because, for example, while planning for action the client may raise new concerns which have to be clarified and understood before the problem can be resolved.

THE SIX-STAGE MODEL

While there are many similarities between the five models presented in Table 3.1 there are also a number of important differences. For example, only two models (those of Lewin and Lippitt *et al.* respectively) make explicit reference to refreezing or stabilising change, although Francis does mention the need to check that the objective has been achieved. Also, only two (those of Lippitt *et al.* and Egan) devote serious attention to the importance of developing and managing an effective helping relationship. The six-stage model presented below draws upon all of these models and integrates their key elements into a framework, or cognitive map, that is both eclectic and practical. The six stages of the helping process are:

1 Developing a helping relationship
2 Helping clients understand the problem situation
3 Helping clients set goals
4 Helping clients plan and take action
5 Consolidating the change
6 Withdrawal

In the second part of this book (starting with Chapter 4) attention will be given to the helping skills that are relevant at each stage of the helping process.

1 Developing a helping relationship

Clients can become aware of an unsatisfactory situation in a number of ways. They may, for example, discover it for themselves because they encounter difficulties maintaining their own performance, acquire new responsibilities that they feel they may not be able to fulfil, or recognise a potential opportunity (such as a new job overseas) but lack the confidence to take advantage of it. Alternatively a problem may be drawn to their attention by their boss, a customer or a colleague.

Problem awareness is not always translated into a desire for help. Some people find it easy to seek or accept help and to share their thoughts with others, whereas some feel reluctant to talk about their problems with anyone. This may be because they fear that others will fail to understand their problems and think that they are incompetent or foolish, or it may be because they fear that seeking help will threaten their autonomy and make them dependent on others.

Relationship building plays an important part in the early stages of the helping process. The helper has to gain the confidence of the client. First impressions can have an important impact on any relationship and studies have shown that clients actively form early impressions of the helper, especially in terms of her competence, ability to offer help, friendliness and inferred motives.

In terms of competence and the ability to help, what some clients want is a helper who has sufficient expertise to be able to see her way through the problem and offer a solution. Expertise is an important source of power which can easily be misused in the helping relationship. As mentioned in Chapter 1, helpers who adopt an advising style may create a relationship in which the client is encouraged to define the helper as expert and then bow to this expertise to the extent that they render themselves helpless.

In terms of friendliness and approachability, what some clients are seeking is a helper who is on the one hand sympathetic to their needs and values, but on the other is sufficiently neutral to offer objective comment and feedback.

In terms of inferred motives, where clients feel they can trust the helper and believe that she is 'on their side' and is 'working for them' they will be more likely to share sensitive information about themselves and, at an appropriate point in the helping relationship, be receptive to feedback or suggestions which draw attention to alternative ways of looking at their problem. However, where the helper is seen as untrustworthy, incompetent and 'not for them', clients will be much more likely to reject feedback and to react defensively to any attempt by the helper to influence their thinking.

Some clients 'test' the helper by presenting what they regard as a safe or peripheral issue to see how the helper responds. If she passes the test and the client feels able to trust the helper he may move on to present the real problem.

2 Helping clients understand the problem situation

This stage is important because problem situations cannot be managed or unused opportunities developed until clients are able to identify and understand them. Egan originally presented the process of identification and clarification as one which involves two steps. These will be referred to here as the inward journey and the outward journey.

The inward journey
The inward journey has four aims: to help clients clarify the nature of their problems; to assist the helper understand what the clients are

concerned about; to reassure the clients that the helper understands their problems; and to facilitate the development of an effective helping relationship. It is concerned with helping clients tell their stories and develop a subjective understanding of their problems. It focuses on how the client sees things; no attempt is made at this stage to persuade clients to consider alternative ways of thinking about their problems.

Consider your own experience of thinking about problems. Many people find that sometimes they mull a problem over in their mind but seem unable to progress their thinking to a point where they are confident that they understand the root cause of their concern. They find themselves locked into a frustrating and unproductive cycle of 'worrying', where they repeatedly reach the same point in their thinking only to find that some block prevents progress and prompts them to start the whole process again. The breakthrough can often come simply as a result of trying to explain the problem to somebody else. Somehow the other person's attentive listening provides the key.

The helper can assist clients clarify their problems *from within their own frames of reference* by attending and responding in ways which help them explore their own feelings, attitudes and behaviours and consider what it is that they do or fail to do which has a bearing on their problems. It is important that the helper empathises with clients, that she shows that she understands what they are saying and how they are feeling from within their own frame of reference.

Empathic listening on the part of the helper not only ensures that she understands the world as her client or clients see it but also involves letting them know that they have been understood from within their own frame of reference. This can be achieved by the helper responding to what has been said. She can reflect back to her clients what it is that she believes they are thinking and feeling and then attend carefully to the cues given off by clients which confirm or deny the accuracy of her responses. Empathy is a core relationship-building skill. It does not involve sympathising with clients and accepting their point of view, but it does involve working hard to understand the problem from the clients' perspective. And clients are much more likely to be open to feedback from someone they feel understands how they see the problem than from someone who does not.

In this stage the helper may also have to persuade clients to *deal with particular and specific issues* if they are to clarify and better understand their problem situations. Vague generalities provide a poor foundation for the generation of strategies to develop unused opportunities or manage problem situations.

A person is being specific in his self-exploration when he identifies and talks about specific experiences, behaviours and feelings that are relevant to his problem. An example of a vague or non-specific statement might be:

'I'm not happy with things at the moment.'

A more specific statement from the same client might be:

'I took up the company's offer of having my own computer and working from home. Sometimes, when I am working alone (*experience*) I begin to feel quite lonely (*feeling*). Finally it gets to me so much that I down tools and go to the pub (*behaviour*), not to drink my sorrows away but just to be with people.'

The helper can assist the client to be more specific by encouraging him to talk (thus increasing the chance that more concrete data will be revealed) and by probing to seek clarification. The theme of listening to the client's experiences, behaviour and feelings is also referred to under the heading 'Following skills' in Chapter 6.

The outward journey

The outward journey is concerned with helping clients consider alternative ways of framing their problem. While the inward journey focuses on helping clients clarify problems from within their own frames of reference, the outward journey focuses on the development of a more objective assessment. Old and comfortable frames of reference may keep clients locked into self-defeating patterns of thinking and behaving, and the helper may need to help them identify blind spots and develop alternative frames of reference.

There are a number of ways the helper can persuade clients to consider their problem situations from alternative perspectives. As they tell their stories the helper may *draw attention to themes*:

'You have mentioned several times, in different ways, that you feel uncomfortable when you have to manage people who have more paper qualifications than you. Is that the way you see it?'

The helper might also draw attention to what appear to be the wider issues:

'The problem doesn't just seem to be that your new boss is a woman, your resentment also seems to be directed at a number of your male colleagues.'

In this phase the helper might also begin constructively to *challenge* clients in those situations where their frames of reference appear to be preventing them from identifying better ways of managing problems. We all have a tendency to think we see things the way they are, and to believe that we are objective in our appraisal of ourselves and our predicament, and this egocentric tendency may prevent clients from fully understanding their problems. The helper can provide clients with *feedback* and *challenge* the way they frame their problems in order to help them develop a more objective understanding of their problem situation.

Motivating clients to act

A key goal of this second stage is to help the client recognise the need for action. Helping clients develop a better understanding of their problems can contribute to this goal, but there is also the possibility of producing the opposite effect. A problem which at first seemed relatively straightforward may begin to appear much more complicated as the client begins to broaden and deepen his understanding of the issues. Lippitt *et al.* note that sometimes the client can begin to feel that the redefined problem is too pervasive and too fundamental to be remedied and therefore may be tempted to give up trying, or may continue working to resolve the problem but in a way which is less receptive to any new information that might further complicate the diagnosis. Often this kind of difficulty can be resolved by helping the client recognise that it may not be possible to deal with all aspects of the problem at once and that it might be necessary to *establish priorities* and work on those issues that will make an important difference. Jackson suggests that a clear definition of the problem is one that enables the client to concentrate on what really matters and helps him to avoid wasting time on irrelevancies. Egan identifies 'focusing' as a vital part of helping clients clarify problem situations. If the diagnostic process reveals several problems or a very complex problem situation it will be necessary to establish some criteria that clients can use to help them decide which aspects of the problem to focus on. Some of the criteria he suggests are: begin with issues the client sees as important and that he is willing to work on; if the problem situation is complex begin with a manageable sub-problem that shows some promise of being successfully handled by the client; and focus on problems where the benefit is likely to outweigh the cost.

3 Goal setting: helping clients develop a more desirable scenario

Insight is seldom sufficient, no matter how interesting it might be. Egan, in *The Skilled Helper*, argues that the aim of the helping relationship is to promote problem-managing and opportunity-taking *action*. He suggests that assessment for the sake of assessment, exploration for the sake of exploration and insight for the sake of insight are close to useless. The previous stage of this helping model (understanding the problem) can only be judged to be effective to the extent that it helps clients construct more desirable scenarios in terms of realistic and achievable goals.

Where attempts to achieve a better understanding of the problem have moved beyond vague and general definitions such as:

'The quality of my working life is deteriorating.'

to an integrated set of more specific definitions such as:

'I am overworked.'

'My subordinates don't get along with each other and I am surrounded by conflicts.'

'I spend too much time away from the office.'

'In my absence problems seem to multiply and nobody seems to care.'

'The company has been reorganised and I have to report to a new boss who is not very supportive.'

'My boss and I have different priorities so I am reluctant to ask her to keep a watching brief in my absence.'

'I seem to have been doing the same old thing for far too long.'

it is easier to move on to the next stage of helping clients identify what a more desirable scenario would look like. A rich definition of the problem not only helps clients identify a more desirable state of affairs, but also offers the possibility of selecting from a range of alternative scenarios. For example, should the manager who wishes to improve the quality of his working life focus attention on being away less, on building a better relationship with his boss so that fewer problems arise during his absences or on finding a new job?

Generating alternatives
All too often people faced with problems fail to think of alternative courses of action. Many people, as soon as they become aware of a problem, are so eager to resolve it that they fail to devote sufficient time to clarifying the problem before dashing off in search of a solution. Jackson, in *The Art of Problem Solving*, refers to this as *solution-mindedness*. Returning to our example, if a manager is experiencing difficulties in getting on with his new boss he may think of solving the problem only in terms of changing jobs and, with this end in mind, might approach a colleague for advice about which job he should accept. He might give no thought to other solutions such as the possibility of taking action to improve the quality of the relationship. The helper (in this case the colleague who has been approached for advice) might usefully intervene by persuading the client to give more thought to what it is that he is trying to achieve. Heirs, in *The Professional Decision Thinker*, argues that managers 'should be thinkers first, doers second – and *equally* competent at both'. This stage of the helping process is concerned with helping clients to be thinkers. The next stage focuses on doing.

The importance of identifying the right goals is illustrated by Covey, who argues in *The Seven Habits of Highly Effective People* that it is incredibly easy to get caught up in an activity trap, in the 'busy-ness' of life, and to work harder and harder at climbing the ladder of success only to discover that it is leaning against the wrong wall. It is possible to be busy, very busy, without being very effective. Effective problem management requires the direction of effort towards the achievement of appropriate goals.

The first goal, objective or solution that comes to mind may not be the best. In the example cited above the manager's first reaction might have been to get out, to find another job. But this was not the only possibility. Clients need to be helped to think about alternative future scenarios. In this case the manager might be asked whether the new job is desired for its own sake or in order to accomplish some other objective. If so, what is this other objective? Why is it important? He might also be asked to think about what would have to be different if the problem were to be solved (or alleviated in some way) and to consider whether, on the one hand, the achievement of the objective (a new job) would bring about these changes and resolve the problem, and, on the other hand, whether these changes might be brought about in some other way. Could these desired changes be secured without changing jobs?

At this stage in the process clients might need help to free their minds from whatever influences are limiting their creativity in order to generate alternative scenarios. Ways of encouraging creative thinking will be addressed in Chapter 9.

Choosing which goal to pursue

Given a range of possible future scenarios, choosing which to pursue is the critical next step. The client has to be motivated to achieve the goal because the course of action necessary to achieve it might require letting go of a number of very satisfying patterns of current behaviour. The loss of these sources of satisfaction may threaten the client's commitment to change and therefore he needs to be confident that the sacrifice will be worth it in the end. Helping clients develop their own criteria for selecting a goal and using these to reach a decision can create a sense of ownership, which can be a powerful source of motivation.

Locke and Latham suggest, in their book *Goal Setting*, that goals can help clients in a number of ways: they provide a vision and a focus for their attention and action; they mobilise energy and effort – people are motivated to achieve goals to which they are committed; goal setting increases persistence – people try harder and are less willing to give up when goals are both clear and realistic; finally, goals provide clients with the motivation to search for strategies that will help them achieve their objective.

4 Helping clients plan and take action

An important measure of the success or failure of the helping relationship is the extent to which the client is able *to take action* to bring about a more desirable state of affairs. While stage 3 of the helping model is concerned with goals (*ends*), this stage is concerned with the *means* of achieving those goals. It involves identifying different strategies for action and selecting and implementing the strategy which offers the greatest promise of success.

An important aspect of the helper's role is to guide clients away from convergent thinking (which leads them to think in terms of only one cause of the problem situation, only one solution to improve matters and only one strategy for achieving that solution) to divergent thinking in which alternative causes, solutions and action plans are explored. Whereas in stage 3 the helper might feel the need to intervene to encourage the client to generate more than one goal, in stage 4 she might intervene to help him think about alternative strategies for achieving the chosen goal.

Techniques such as brainstorming and synectics can provide a useful aid for helping clients identify different ways of achieving goals, and the chosen route may well end up comprising a combination of the best ideas derived from a number of different action plans.

Another important aspect of the helper's role is to guide the client away from vague generalities towards specific thinking. At an early stage of the helping process the helper might need to encourage the client to think in terms of specific issues and factors that contribute to his predicament. At a later stage attention may shift to thinking in terms of specific goals and targets or change rather than vague and non-specific aims. Finally, in the fourth stage of the helping process, the helper might need to encourage the client to think in terms of specific actions that need to be taken if these goals are to be achieved.

Force-field analysis offers an approach to systematically searching out viable courses of action. It is a method, based on the work of Lewin (mentioned at the beginning of this chapter), for identifying the psychological and social forces which affect behaviour, for identifying how the forces opposing change can be diminished and how the forces pushing for change can be strengthened, and for thinking about the development of an action plan that takes account of the secondary effects associated with manipulating both kinds of forces. Force-field analysis will be considered in greater detail in Chapter 10.

In a few cases the need for detailed planning may be minimal. Where the problem is relatively straightforward it is possible that the exploration and analysis that was involved in identifying specific goals for action might point to an obvious course of action. It might be, for example, that an instruction to a subordinate to introduce a simple screening procedure might solve a manager's problem by eliminating the need for him to be involved in a time-consuming complaints procedure that diverts his attention away from more rewarding activities.

All too often, however, the importance of planning detailed specific actions is underestimated. How do you achieve the goal of improving the quality of your relationship with an unsupportive boss who does not share your priorities? In this kind of case it may not be enough for the client to have generated a range of possible strategies and selected the one which offered the greatest promise of success. It might be necessary to help him develop a step-by-step programme for action which includes establishing milestones and measures of success that can be used to assess whether each step has been achieved.

It may also be necessary to develop some contingency plans in case the planned action fails to produce the anticipated results. This need for contingency planning is especially important because often the helper cannot be present to 'coach' the client while he is implementing his action plan. The helper can help the client decide what he plans to do. She can also review what happened after the client implemented a part of the plan. But she is unlikely to be there to offer continuous feedback and support. If things do not go according to plan the client may have to decide how to respond without any assistance from the helper.

The aim of this stage of planning and taking action, therefore, is to help the client develop a sufficiently detailed plan, with appropriate milestones, measures of success and contingency plans, to facilitate *independent* action.

5 Consolidating the change

It was noted earlier that sometimes a client might achieve a goal but fail to sustain the behaviour necessary to maintain this preferred scenario. Lippitt *et al.* argue in *The Dynamics of Planned Change* that one of the important questions about any change process is whether or not the change that has been accomplished will remain a stable and permanent part of the social system. They state that too often change which has been produced by painstaking and costly effort tends to disappear after the change effort has ceased. Even though the motivation to change was there and the goal was accomplished, the change has no permanence and the system slips back into its old ways.

Consolidating change requires the continued motivation of the client and one way of achieving this is through the availability of relevant feedback on a regular basis. In those situations where feedback on the effect of new initiatives is not available it can become difficult for the client to judge whether any further action is necessary to maintain the change. It may be that some new behaviours which at first were successful in securing and maintaining the desired change begin to lose some of their potency, but the client may be unaware of this because of inadequate feedback. Even where the client is aware that remedial action is required the lack of feedback may make it difficult to assess the effectiveness of any new initiatives.

In those circumstances where the action plan has been successful in bringing about a more desirable state of affairs, lack of feedback on the efficacy of specific activities may lead the client to believe that they are ineffective, unimportant and not worth the effort. Consequently the client may no longer make the effort, thus undermining the success of the change effort.

The helper might be able to contribute to the consolidation of change by helping the client identify possible sources of feedback that already exist or by encouraging him to develop new sources of feedback for himself, such as setting up review meetings with significant others, developing new statistical indicators or implementing a regular survey of customer or employee attitudes.

6 Withdrawal

If the aim of helping is to empower others to act on their own behalf then the helper has, at some point, to withdraw and leave the client to act on his own. Some clients will need less help than others, therefore the helper needs to monitor, on a regular basis, whether she has reached the point where she should disengage.

One client may be finding it difficult to manage a problem situation because his diagnosis of the situation is hampered by his inability to identify and understand how his own behaviour is contributing to the situation. A supportive intervention that encourages him to tell his story and develop for himself a better understanding of the problem may be the only help he requires. Given this understanding he may be perfectly capable of solving the problem for himself and the helper may be able to terminate her helping relationship with the client.

Another client may need to be helped to develop alternative ways of looking at his problem. The helper may need to challenge discrepancies between what the client appears to value and the way he behaves, or between the way he sees himself and the way he is regarded by others, before he can reach an adequate understanding of his predicament. Furthermore, while help in developing a better understanding of the problem might be necessary it may not be sufficient for the client to act independently to manage his own problem more effectively. He may also need help setting goals and planning action.

A third client may have a clear and appropriate goal he wants to achieve but may lack the ability to transform his intentions into actual change efforts. In this case the helper might feel able to confine her intervention to stage 4 of the model, which is concerned with taking action.

In other words, some clients may require help with every stage of problem management (understanding the problem, goal setting, planning and taking action, and consolidation) whereas others may require help only with particular stages. The six-stage helping model presented here provides a map that can be used to assess where the client is and what help he requires. Armed with this the helper can decide when it would be appropriate to withdraw and leave the client to get on with managing his own life.

This chapter opened with the proposition that if helping is defined in terms of assisting others to become more proactive in the management of their own problems the helper needs to have an understanding of the essential steps in the problem management process and needs to be aware of how she can intervene to help clients help themselves. The steps of the helping process have been elaborated within the context of a six-stage model of helping. The six stages are:

1   Developing a helping relationship
2   Helping clients understand the problem situation:

The inward journey – helping clients understand the problem from within their frame of reference
The outward journey – helping clients develop new perspectives
Motivating clients to act

3   Helping clients set goals:

Helping clients generate alternative scenarios
Helping clients choose which goal to pursue

4   Helping clients plan and take action
5   Consolidating the change
6   Withdrawing from the helping relationship

EXERCISE 3.2: REVIEW OF THE HELPING PROCESS

Compare the stages of this six-stage model with the steps you identified in Exercise 3.1. Reflect on any differences and consider how this model could be used to guide your helping interventions.

Part II
Developing helping skills

4   *Helping skills: an overview*

Part I of this book considered the nature of helping and advocated an approach to helping which involves helping others to help themselves. Part II focuses attention on the skills that an effective helper needs to use.

Helping involves the use of many different skills, but these skills are not special skills reserved for the helping relationship. They are skills that are important in many kinds of relationship. Sometimes people are less effective helpers than they might be because they are unaware of the importance of, or lack competence in, some of these 'everyday skills'. This chapter will focus attention on some of the most important skills that are required by the skilled helper.

It might be useful to begin by thinking about the people who have tried to help you in the past and trying to recall what it was that they did that was either helpful or unhelpful.

EXERCISE 4.1: HELPING SKILLS

Helpful behaviour Identify an occasion when somebody was very helpful and try to remember what it was that they did that was so helpful. List the helpful behaviours and make a note of why you felt that they were helpful.	
How did the helper behave, what did he or she do?	What was the effect of this behaviour?

Behaviour that did not help Identify an occasion when somebody was *not* very helpful (or may even have made the problem situation more difficult to manage) and try to remember what it was that they did that was so unhelpful.	
How did the helper behave, what did he or she do?	What was the effect of this behaviour?

While it is unlikely that any of the unhelpful behaviours listed above would find their way into your catalogue of helping skills, it is possible that they may point to important helping skills because unhelpful behaviours can be the antithesis or reverse side of helpful behaviours. Bearing this in mind, review your lists of helpful and unhelpful behaviours and consider whether the skills they suggest can be grouped together to produce a shorter list of generic skills. If so, what labels would you use to describe these skills?

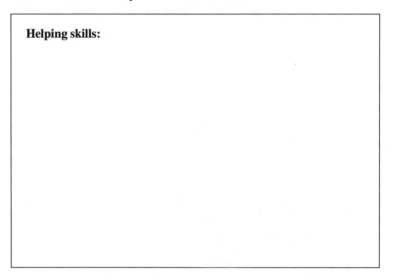

Helping skills:

You might like to compare your list of skills with those presented in this chapter. Remember the point that was made in the opening paragraph, that helping skills are not a special set of skills reserved for the helping relationship. Helping involves many interpersonal skills that are used in a wide range of other relationships. Those considered here are the skills which the author and others believe are some of the most important, but no claim is made that they represent a fully inclusive list. However, if your list includes skills that are not mentioned here you might wish to consider how and where they fit into the model of the helping process presented in Chapter 3. If your list does not include some of the skills that are mentioned in this chapter you might feel it necessary to challenge the author's view that they are important, or you may feel that your list should be modified to include them.

HELPING SKILLS

The helper has to be competent in a number of interpersonal and intrapersonal skills. In order to get started she has to have the skills necessary to build an effective helping relationship with her clients. 'Client' in this context means anybody who is the recipient of help. The only relationship some potential clients may have with the helper may be a helping relationship. In many instances, however, the client may be a person the helper interacts with in other circumstances. He may be a friend, a member of the family or a work colleague. It will be necessary for the helper to pay careful attention to the development of the helping relationship even where she has another ongoing relationship with the potential client. The helper needs to be able to develop a relationship in which the client will be willing to share his problems and be receptive to appropriate influence. This is not always easy. Many parents, for example, do not have this kind of relationship with their children and many children do not have this kind of relationship with their parents. You might find it useful to reflect on why this might be. Could it be that a parent is too ashamed to disclose a problem to his child, or fears that seeking help will undermine the existing parent–child relationship that is so important to the parent? What other barriers might there be?

Similar problems will arise elsewhere. In the workplace it may be difficult for a subordinate to seek help from his boss or a manager to seek help from a colleague.

The helper has to be able to communicate to the client that she is not about to judge him, that she is willing to work hard at understanding the problem from within his frame of reference and that she is on his side – not in the sense that she will necessarily accept his point of view when she has understood what that is, but in the sense that she is 'for the client' and is willing to work with him to help him improve his ability to manage the problem situation more effectively. This involves showing respect for the client and listening, empathically, to what he has to say. *Empathic listening contributes to relationship building, but it also has an important role in every other stage of the helping process.*

In the second stage of the helping process ('Helping the client develop a better understanding of his problem') the helper needs to be able to encourage the client to tell his story. She can do this, and gently seek out more information from the client, by using a range of micro skills which will be considered in more detail in Chapter 6, 'Listening'.

When clients tell their stories they may present an incomplete or confusing picture and the helper may have to press for more information and encourage the client to explore the problem more thoroughly and in more concrete terms. Some important skills that can facilitate this will be considered in Chapter 7, 'Probing for information'.

In order to help the client develop a more objective assessment of his problem (in the phase of the model referred to as the outward journey) the helper may need to alert him to the possibility of framing his problem in different ways. This might involve drawing the client's attention to themes he might not have recognised and helping him see 'the bigger picture'. Some of the skills that this involves will also be considered in Chapter 6.

In order to develop a more objective assessment of the problem it might also be necessary to help the client identify blind spots and provide him with feedback which offers new information that he may wish to consider. In addition, the helper might feel it necessary to confront some of the assumptions that underpin the client's definition of his problem These helping skills will be considered in Chapter 8, 'Offering feedback and challenging assumptions'.

Another skill that is important is a largely *intra*personal skill concerned with self-awareness. The importance of self-awareness was stressed at the end of Chapter 1. Unless the helper is aware of her own values and assumptions and how these affect her approach to helping, and is receptive to feedback from others which will facilitate an assessment of how effective her interventions have been, she may not only be less effective than she could be, but also may add to the client's problems without realising it. The next chapter will discuss the helper's awareness of her own values and Chapter 8 will consider the helper's need for and receptivity to feedback on her effectiveness.

In addition to the interpersonal and intrapersonal skills mentioned above, the skilled helper may also need to be able to help the client to be more creative when thinking about goals and strategies for achieving goals, and to be more systematic when developing detailed action plans. Many of the skills already considered will be relevant here but, in addition, some techniques that the helper may find useful will be presented in Chapter 9, 'Encouraging creative thinking', and

Chapter 10, 'A force-field approach to developing action plans'.
The main helping skills referred to in this chapter are:

- Self-awareness
- Establishing rapport and building relationships
- Empathy
- Listening to facts and feelings
- Probing for information
- Identifying themes and seeing the bigger picture
- Giving feedback
- Challenging assumptions

They will be considered in more detail in the following chapters.

5 Self-awareness and core values

An important aspect of helper self-awareness is the helper's ability to develop a clear understanding of her values and assumptions and how these influence her approach to helping. Covey, in his book *The Seven Habits of Highly Effective People*, argues that the more aware people are of their basic 'paradigms, maps and assumptions' and the extent to which they have been influenced by their own experience, the more they can take responsibility for their paradigms, examine them, test them against reality, listen to others and be open to their perceptions, thereby gaining a larger picture and a far more objective view. Helpers need to have this kind of objective view of themselves and their approach to helping.

Helpers who lack self-awareness may be unaware of their own values and how they affect the way they behave when helping, and how others interpret and react to their interventions.

A number of writers appear to agree that there are two core values that are shared by those people who have been recognised as being effective helpers. Rogers, in *Client Centered Therapy*, labelled these *unconditional positive regard for the client* (more often referred to as *respect*) and *genuineness*. Unconditional positive regard is important because if the helper's support is conditional clients may not feel free to express themselves fully and may suppress and distort experiences that they suspect will be unacceptable to the helper. Unconditional positive regard does not necessarily involve approval but it does involve acceptance and respect.

RESPECT

Egan, in *The Skilled Helper*, and Reddy, in *The Manager's Guide to Counselling at Work*, elaborate the core value of respect to include:

Being 'for' the client. This involves the helper behaving in a manner which indicates that she is 'with' or 'for' the client in a non-sentimental caring way. If the client feels the helper might be against him he is unlikely to put his trust in her or reveal anxieties, weaknesses or specific information that he fears could be used against him.

Signalling that the other's viewpoint is worth listening to. This reflects the helper's willingness to commit herself to working with the client. It also suggests a minimum level of openness to the other's point of view. Without this openness empathic listening is impossible. Too often, even when we go through the motions of asking the other for their view, we are not really committed to listening. For example, a parent, before visiting his wrath upon a child, might ask for an explanation of her behaviour, but even though he asks he may not really expect to receive a satisfactory explanation, and therefore may not prepare himself to listen to what the child has to say. Reddy cites an example in which the parent realises at the last minute that what the child has to say is important. From her perspective the behaviour in question makes perfect sense and deserves praise, not punishment. The effective helper needs to listen to and respect the client's point of view and needs to clearly signal this respect if the client is to be encouraged to work with the helper.

Suspending critical judgement. The helper needs to keep an open mind and avoid reaching premature conclusions. This does not mean that the helper should signal approval of everything she hears or observes, rather that she should communicate that she understands the client's point of view. Reddy suggests that communicating understanding in this way helps the client change because rather than pushing him into a position that he may resist, by suspending judgement and trying to understand the other's viewpoint the helper can offer him the opportunity to explore his position and give him the freedom to change his view. This approach is in line with the argument advanced by Lewin (reported near the beginning of

Chapter 3) that the most effective way of bringing about change is to work at diminishing the forces that oppose or resist it rather than pushing and increasing the pressures for change.

According to Reddy, suspending judgement and keeping an open mind does not come naturally to many people because we have all been conditioned to persuade others to our point of view. At school there is nearly always a debating society but rarely a listening club. It may be that we often fail to keep an open mind because we fear that if we listen we might end up agreeing, and if we agree we may appear to have lost. In the helping relationship, however, the aim is not to win. It is to help the client develop the capability to manage his problems for himself. Suspending judgement can contribute to the achievement of this goal because it encourages the client to believe that the helper is 'for' him and has his interests at heart.

Working with the client as a unique individual. This involves being willing to support each client in his or her uniqueness and not relating with them as just another 'case'. It requires the helper to personalise the helping process and tailor it to the needs, capabilities and resources of each client.

Respecting the client's right to determine his own fate. The role of the helper is to help the client develop a sense of agency or self-efficacy rather than to promote a state of dependency and a feeling of helplessness. This implies an attitude, on the part of the helper, that the client does have the resources necessary to managing his problems more effectively. The helper's role is to facilitate the development of these resources. It is not the helper's role to take over the client's problems and prescribe solutions. If the client opts for a course of action which the helper feels does not offer the best way forward she might encourage him to think again, to challenge his own solution, but ultimately the helper needs to respect the client's right to determine his own fate.

Assuming that the client is committed to the goal of managing his problems more effectively. It has already been noted that some clients may not have referred themselves for help and might engage in the helping relationship with some reluctance. For example, the sales representative who has had a poor appraisal may be required to work more closely with his manager so that she can help him improve his performance. He may resent being told that his performance is not up to the required standard and may be, at least initially, reluctant to work more closely with his manager in order that she can help him. However, in this case the initial reluctance to work with the helper does not necessarily imply that the sales representative is not committed to finding ways of managing his own problems more effectively. He might be desperate to do something about it. Egan suggests that respectful helpers will assume the client's goodwill and will continue to work with him until this assumption has clearly been demonstrated to be false. A client who recognises that the helper respects him and is oriented to his needs is more likely to engage positively in the helping relationship than one who observes little evidence of respect.

GENUINENESS

Rogers argues, in *Client Centered Therapy*, that the helper should develop a genuine relationship with the client. This is important in the helping relationship because if respect for the client is faked and if such attitudes as openness and interest in the client are not genuine then there is a high probability that the client will detect it and that it will seriously damage or even destroy the helping relationship. Being genuine involves being honest, sincere and without façade even if this involves being frank and confronting the client. Egan defines genuineness as a value that can be expressed as a set of behaviours which include being oneself, being open, spontaneous, assertive and consistent. He also argues that being genuine involves working at behaviours that help clients. He suggests that clients can become annoyed when helpers seem so relaxed that their ease can be interpreted as lack of interest. On the other hand they will not be comfortable with the helping relationship if they experience the helper as uptight. Egan believes that genuine helpers are comfortable with what they are doing because they are good at what they are doing. Over time they need to become skilled at and comfortable with the behaviours which help clients, even if these behaviours are not a part of their natural style. The following chapters focus attention on these behaviours and consider how the helper can become more skilled in their use.

BECOMING MORE SELF-AWARE

Working at the behaviours that help clients (that is, working at developing helping skills) requires the helper to know herself and the effect her behaviour has on others – it requires self-awareness. Developing a heightened sense of self-awareness involves being sensitive to the feedback provided by clients and it involves being able to observe oneself and generate one's own feedback. Exercise 5.1 suggests a way of doing this.

EXERCISE 5.1: BECOMING MORE AWARE OF YOUR VALUES

Next time you are involved in a helping relationship try to open a 'second channel' so that, as well as listening to the client, you can listen to yourself. Not only to what you are saying but also to what you are thinking.

As you listen to yourself, monitor your thoughts and what they tell you about your values. Are you able to suspend critical judgement? Do you really believe that the client's point of view is worth listening to? Is what you are thinking and saying consistent with the value that the client has the right to determine his own fate?

It may be relatively easy to subscribe to a set of 'core values' when they are listed in a book, and you may be willing to integrate them into your espoused theory of helping, but are they reflected in your theory in use? If your values in use are different from your espoused values you might wish to consider what you need to do about it.

6 *Listening*

People often complain that they have been misunderstood: 'She never listens', 'It's like talking to a brick wall', 'I could tell she wasn't listening'. How can you tell when somebody is not listening, and what are the reasons why sometimes (often?) people are not as good at listening as they could be? Exercise 6.1 looks for answers to these questions from your own experience.

EXERCISE 6.1: POOR LISTENERS

Think of at least two occasions when you felt that somebody was not really listening to what you had to say. Picture each of these occasions clearly in your mind and:

(a) List what it was that the other person *did* that gave you the feeling that they were not really listening.

continued

(b) Think of the reasons which might have explained why the 'listener' was not listening very effectively.

It might also be useful to think about some of the factors which contribute to good listening. Recall at least two occasions when you were confident that someone was listening carefully to what you had to say.

EXERCISE 6.2: GOOD LISTENERS

Think of at least two occasions when you felt that somebody was really listening to what you had to say. Picture each of these occasions clearly in your mind and:

(a) List what it was that the other person *did* that gave you the feeling that they were really listening.

continued

(b) Think of some of the reasons which might have explained why the 'listener' was listening effectively.

This chapter is about what makes a good listener. It will consider the kind of listening that is important in the helping relationship, examine some of the barriers to effective listening and what the helper can do to minimise their effect, and it will focus attention on some of the behaviours that can contribute to effective listening. You might like to test the validity of the content of this chapter against your own experience as recorded in your answers to Exercises 6.1 and 6.2.

EMPATHIC LISTENING

Listening involves more than just hearing what somebody has to say. It involve searching for a full and accurate understanding of the other's message. But searching for the meaning of the other's message is not something which everybody finds easy to do all of the time. Consider the following conversation between a manager and her subordinate:

Manager: Hello Jim, are you all right? You are not looking yourself today.
Jim: I'm OK.
Manager: Are you sure?
Jim: I don't want to bother you.
Manager: It's no bother, tell me about it.
Jim: I've just got my exam results and I've failed a paper on the part-time MBA that I'm doing in the evenings. I

shouldn't have failed but things are in such a mess here that I've had to work over and miss some classes.

Manager: Don't upset yourself, it isn't worth it. I've done all right for myself and I don't even have a first degree. If you were to put all of your energy into your job rather than wasting it on yet another course you would get on a lot faster.

EXERCISE 6.3

> Can you think of a better alternative to the manager's last statement?

This conversation got off to a good start. The manager responded to the non-verbal messages that her subordinate was 'giving off', and all appeared to be going well until it became evident that the manager was not empathising with Jim and was not listening to what he was saying from within his frame of reference. She was listening to what he was saying from within her own frame of reference. And from her perspective what she heard suggested that her subordinate was faced with an opportunity (to get rid of distractions and refocus his efforts). She failed to understand the problem from his perspective before rushing in with a possible solution.

Empathic listening demonstrates the helper's respect for the client and gives the client confidence in the helper. Covey, in *The Seven Habits of Highly Effective People*, argues that empathic listening is so powerful because it provides the helper with accurate data to work with. Instead of the helper 'progressing her own autobiography and assuming thoughts, feelings, motives and interpretation' she is able to deal with the reality inside the other person's head and heart. Empathising with others means seeing the world as they see it and understanding how they feel as well as how they think about issues.

BARRIERS TO EFFECTIVE LISTENING

There is a limit to how much information a person can attend to at any one time. In the workplace a maintenance engineer may not listen to what an operator is trying to tell her about his machine because she may be preoccupied with something else. For example, she might be trying to overhear what the departmental manager is saying to a stranger in the corner of the room, looking out of the window and watching a lorry that is reversing towards her car in the car park, or preoccupied with a pain down her left arm. Any or all of these competing stimuli might receive more attention than the operator's problem. She might be interested in what the manager is saying to the stranger because it might have something to do with the rumour that consultants have been brought in to reorganise the factory and reduce the wage bill. She might be concerned about the lorry because she fears that it might collide with her new car. She might be preoccupied by the pain because she has very high blood pressure and both her sister and mother died after heart attacks.

Even if the engineer does listen to the operator's problem she may not fully understand what she is being told. What she hears might be different from what the operator thinks he has told her. The operator may use jargon that is foreign to the engineer, or may so complicate the story with unnecessary detail that she is unable to identify the root problem. Sometimes expectations influence how a person can interpret a situation. Covey illustrates this with a story told by Frank Koch, published in *Proceedings*, the magazine of the Naval Institute.

Two battleships assigned to the training squadron had been at sea on manoeuvres in heavy weather for several days. I was serving on the lead battleship and was on watch on the bridge as night fell. The visibility was poor with patchy fog, so the captain remained on the bridge keeping an eye on all activities.

Shortly after dark, the lookout on the wing of the bridge reported, 'Light bearing on the starboard bow.'

'Is it steady or moving astern?', the captain called out.

Lookout replied, 'Steady, captain,' which meant we were on a dangerous collision course with that ship.

The captain then called to the signal man, 'Signal that ship:

"We are on a collision course, advise you change course 20 degrees."'

Back came a signal, 'Advisable for you to change course 20 degrees.'

The captain said, 'Send, "I'm a captain, change course 20 degrees."'

'I'm a seaman second class,' came the reply. 'You had better change course 20 degrees.'

By that time the captain was furious. He spat out, 'Send, "I'm a battleship. Change course 20 degrees."'

Back came the flashing light, 'I'm a lighthouse.'

We changed course.

The captain had expected the light to be from another ship and this expectation influenced the way he interpreted the messages he received.

Another source of misunderstandings is the failure to pay attention to every part of the message. The listener may be inattentive because the speaker pauses from time to time while searching for the right words, and during these pauses she may be tempted to let her mind wander and to think about other things. Misunderstandings arise when these 'other things' turn out to be so interesting that she continues to think about them even when the speaker has started to talk again. Sometimes a helper may fail to pay attention to all of the message because she thinks she understands the message before the client has finished speaking and she begins to formulate a reply. Exercise 6.4 might illustrate this.

EXERCISE 6.4: LISTENING TO PART OF THE MESSAGE, PART 1

What picture comes into your mind as you read the following words?

WOMAN, TABLE, KNIFE, CLOTH

Describe it below.

The second part of this exercise is presented on the next page.

LISTENING SKILLS

The aim of the remaining part of the chapter is to identify and elaborate the skills needed by the helper in order to improve her ability to listen effectively. This involves developing the skills which:

(a) help the client 'tell his story' to the best of his ability;
(b) keep the helper's attention focused on the client's message;
(c) assist the helper to organise the information she receives so that she can make sense of even complex or badly structured messages; and
(d) ensure that the helper has understood the client's message.

The skilled helper needs to be skilled at attending to both the factual and affective content of a message. She should neither ignore nor be overwhelmed by the client's emotion and she needs to be able to interpret what is said in a way that reflects accurately what the client is thinking and feeling about the content of the message.

Listening skills will be discussed under three headings: attending, following and reflecting.

EXERCISE 6.4: PART 2

Are the following four words consistent with the scene you described above?

EMERGENCY, SURGEON, BLOOD, INTESTINES

When people fail to listen to all of the message they can fail to understand what they have been told. The eight words woman, table, knife, cloth, emergency, surgeon, blood and intestines offer a consistent message, but it is not unusual for people who heard only the first four words to develop a very different picture from the one they would have had if they had heard all eight words. Do you ever fail to listen to all of the message?

1 Attending

An important set of listening skills are concerned with letting the client know that the helper is with him. Everybody, at some time or other, has been told by a friend or colleague that they have not been listening. If somebody has ever said this to you, you may have been able to leap to your own defence by repeating most of what your accuser had said. You may have heard, you may even have been able to repeat the message like a tape recorder, but if the truth were known you may not have been really listening and this fact may have been apparent to the speaker.

People want to feel that the helper is genuinely interested in what they have to say and that she will work hard to understand their message. It will be more difficult to develop rapport, and the client will be much less likely to give a full account of himself, if he feels that the person from whom he is seeking help is preoccupied and uninterested.

The helper is constantly giving out cues and messages with her body. Egan argues that by being mindful of the cues and messages she is sending the helper can deliberately develop and project an image that tells the speaker that she is 'with him'. Egan, in *The Skilled Helper*, offers the mnemonic **SOLER** as an aid to remembering ways in which the listener can project a sense of presence.

S: Face the speaker **S**quarely. This is a basic posture of involvement which tells the client that the helper is with him. Sitting 'squarely' need not be taken too literally. In some situations an anxious client might be overpowered by too much attention so a slight angling of the position might be called for, but if the listener turns too far away the message she communicates might be one of indifference or rejection. We have all heard the expression 'he gave me the cold shoulder'.

O: Adopt an **O**pen posture. Tightly crossed arms or legs can communicate to the client that the helper is in a defensive mood and/ or not open to influence. Uncrossed or loosely crossed limbs communicate a sense of openness and approachability.

L: **L**ean the upper part of your body towards the speaker. A slight inclination of the listener's body towards the client communicates interest and attention. An enthralled audience can sometimes be described as 'sitting on the edge of their seats'. Leaning backwards or slouching can be taken to mean that the helper is not in tune with the client or is bored by the message she is hearing. As with facing the speaker squarely, leaning too far forward can be overpowering in some circumstances. The good listener is alert to feedback which tells her whether to lean more towards the client or to back off slightly at different points in the interaction.

E: Maintaining good **E**ye contact with the client is one of the most powerful ways of communicating that the listener is with him and wants to hear what he has to say. Good eye contact does not mean maintaining a hard, fixed stare. That can project an image of hostile confrontation. To communicate involvement the eyes should be focused softly on the speaker's face and, rather than maintaining uninterrupted contact, the gaze should shift occasionally, to a gesturing hand or to the notes the client might have in front of him, and then return to his face. Looking away, especially if this happens too frequently, signals that the helper is not involved. Consider how you feel when talking to somebody who keeps glancing over your shoulder to look at other people in the room or who keeps glancing at her watch or the clock on the wall! Taken to an extreme, the almost total absence of eye contact usually signals indifference or boredom. Many people are passive listeners. They pay close attention to what is being said but they doodle on their pad or look out of the window while the client is talking. Although they are listening, the message which the client receives is that they 'don't want to know'. This can be very inhibiting for the client and is one of the reasons why it is useful to think in terms of 'active' as opposed to 'passive' listening. The helper can be considerably more effective if she engages actively in the process of listening.

R: Try to be relatively **R**elaxed while engaging in these behaviours: if the helper is too tense or nervous the client will not feel at ease. The aim is to be neither so relaxed and laid back that the client feels the helper is not prepared to work at understanding what he has to say, nor so tense that he is frightened off and disinclined to talk. What is required is the projection of a relaxed but alert posture which suggests both a comfortable relationship and a genuine interest in what the client has to say. The helper who is too tense is likely to hold her body too still and create an impression of being very controlled and aloof. Smooth movement, especially if it responds to and reflects what the speaker is saying, suggests listening with empathic understanding.

The **SOLER** mnemonic offers a set of pointers to the kind of behaviour which communicates a sense of presence to the client. These need not always be adhered to strictly. They are not rules, rather they are reminders of the importance of non-verbal behaviour. The helper's body is a vehicle for communication and she should constantly be aware of all the cues and messages she is sending. This point is developed later in this chapter, when consideration is also given to how the helper can interpret the non-verbal behaviour of the client.

Compare the attending skills discussed here with your responses to Exercises 6.1 and 6.2.

2 Following skills

Bolton, in *People Skills*, argues that while one of the primary tasks of the listener is to stay out of the other's way so that the listener can discover how the speaker views his situation, this aim is often frustrated because the 'listener' interrupts and diverts the speaker by asking too many questions or making too many statements. All too often this happens in the helping relationship because the helper does too much of the talking.

The helper can encourage the client to talk, can better concentrate on the task of listening and can gently seek out more information to help promote a better understanding of the client's problem by using door openers, minimal prompts, accents, attentive silences and a number of special concentration techniques as well as by making statements and asking questions.

Door openers

Careful attention to non-verbal clues can often signal when some-body is preoccupied or worried and may want to talk. In these circumstances the helper might be able to initiate the helping process by offering what Bolton describes as a non-coercive invitation to talk; this might be either an invitation to begin a conversation or an encouragement to continue if the speaker shows signs that he is unsure about saying more. The manager's opening remarks in the case presented near the beginning of this chapter offer an example of how door openers can be used. Bolton suggests that door openers typically have four elements:

(a) A description of the other person's body language, for example:
'You are not looking yourself today.'
'You sound a bit low.'
(b) An invitation to talk or continue talking:
'Feel like talking?'
'Do you want to tell me about it?'
(c) Silence – not rushing the other person but giving him time to decide.
(d) Attending – engaging in the attending behaviours already discussed, especially eye contact and a positive involvement that demonstrates the listener's interest in and concern for the other person.

Door openers will not always receive a positive response. A potential client may be reluctant to talk. However, it can sometimes be helpful to encourage a reluctant client with more than one non-coercive invitation to talk (as in the case presented on page 70), but remember that door openers should be perceived as non-coercive and the reluctant client must not be pushed too hard. A relationship can be seriously damaged if the over-eager helper attempts to coerce a reluctant client.

Minimal prompts
Hackney and Cormier suggest, in their book *Counselling Strategies and Objectives*, that the helper often uses 'minimal verbal activity' as a reinforcer or prompt to further exploration. In conversation prompts such as 'uh-huh', 'right', 'mmm', 'really', 'yes', 'and ...', 'tell me more', 'wow', can signal to the client that you are listening and can encourage him to continue. Sometimes, on the telephone, if the listener has remained silent too long, the speaker feels the need to ask 'Are you still there?' In face-to-face conversation a minimal prompt can take the form of a gesture, a nod of the head or a slight inclination of the body.

Bolton makes the point that minimal prompts do not imply agreement or disagreement. 'Yes' means 'yes, I hear what you are saying, go on' rather than 'yes, I agree with what you are saying'. The purpose of the minimal prompt is to let the client know that he has been heard and that the helper would be interested to hear more. It is not used to offer a judgement on what the client is saying.

The 'accent'
Another response that can help uncover relevant information is what Hackney and Cormier refer to as the accent. They define it as 'a one or two word restatement that focuses or brings attention to a preceding client response'. For example:

Manager: 'Most of the customer reports seemed OK'.
Colleague: '*Seemed* OK?'
Manager: 'Well, I suppose I'd hoped for better. What I had expected was that ...'

The 'accent' can be used to encourage others to say more fully what they have only half said or hinted at.

Statements

If the helper asks too many questions the client might end up feeling that he is being interrogated. Asking questions and probing for information will be considered in more detail in Chapter 7 but an alternative to some questions might be the kind of statement that make a demand on the client to say more, to elaborate or clarify. For example, the statement:

'What you have been saying seems to have made you very angry.'

might encourage the speaker to talk about his feelings of anger without feeling that he is being quizzed.

Infrequent questions

Many helpers make an excessive and inappropriate use of questions. Often such questions are used to yield information related to the concerns of the helper rather than those of the client. This kind of self-centred questioning might be useful when the aim of the listener is to better comprehend information that will be of use to her later or to evaluate the worth of another's persuasive argument but it is less appropriate when the listener is using questions in an attempt to understand accurately the thoughts and feelings of the speaker.

With empathic listening, questions can be used to good effect when the helper has not followed what the client has been saying or when she feels a need for more information in order to develop a better understanding of the client's point of view. They can also be used to provide a useful prompt to encourage the client to think a little more deeply about what he has been saying. For example:

'Could you say a little more about why you felt the negotiations broke down?'

Attentive silences

Helpers sometimes ask too many questions because they cannot cope with even a short silence. They need to fill the gap.

Learning the art of silent responsiveness has been described as the key to good listening. Bolton, in *People Skills*, suggests that a silence can give the speaker time to consider what to say. It enables him to go deeper into himself and examine his thoughts. Whether or not the client is using the silence for this purpose can often be detected by the direction of his gaze. If, when he stops talking, the client fails to make any eye contact with the helper, this is likely to be a sign that he is thinking and that in time he will continue talking. If, on the other hand, he stops talking and looks towards the helper, he is probably signalling that he has finished and now it is her turn. The helper might respond to this cue with a statement or a question or she might allow the silence to continue in order gently to nudge the client into saying more. A silence used in this way can be a powerful prompt, especially if it is accompanied with any of the non-verbal behaviours which indicate that the client has the helper's full attention and she is waiting to hear more.

Aids to concentration
The helper can improve her ability to follow what the client is saying by using one of a number of techniques which aid concentration. Hargie *et al.*, in *Social Skills in Interpersonal Communication*, discuss the use of intrapersonal dialogue. The helper concentrates on what the client is saying and heightens her receptivity by asking herself questions such as 'why is he telling me this now?' or engaging in covert coaching and telling herself whenever she is not paying enough attention. Intrapersonal dialogue involves opening the kind of 'second channel' suggested in Exercise 5.1.

The helper might also find the kind of listening framework proposed by Egan in *The Skilled Helper*, which focuses attention on experiences, behaviours and feelings, a helpful aid to concentration as well as providing a useful structure within which to organise incoming information. This kind of framework can also suggest areas that might be explored beneficially with the client. Egan suggests people talk about:

Experiences – that is, what happens to them. If a client tells you he was fired from his job, he is talking about his problem situation in terms of an experience.

Behaviours – that is, what do they do or fail to do. If a client tells you he has sex with underage boys, he is talking about his problem situation in terms of his behaviour.

Affect – that is, the feelings and emotions that arise from or are associated with either experiences or behaviour. If a client tells you how depressed he gets after drinking bouts, he is talking about the affect associated with his problem situation.

Egan advocates the use of this framework to help clients clarify their problem situation or explore their unused opportunities. If the listening task involves a personal problem Egan believes that it will be clear to both client and helper when it is seen and understood in terms of specific experiences, specific behaviours and specific feelings and emotions.

> *Compare the following skills discussed here with your responses to Exercises 6.1 and 6.2.*

3 Reflecting

A reflective response, according to Bolton in *People Skills*, is when the listener restates the feeling and/or content of what the client has communicated and does so in a way that demonstrates understanding and acceptance. This kind of restatement not only provides an opportunity to check that the client has been understood, but can also help the client clarify his own thoughts.

Understanding is not easily achieved, especially if it is to include an awareness of what the message means to the speaker. Defined in this way, understanding involves the helper taking the client's perspective into account. Deetz and Stevenson suggest, in *Managing Interpersonal Communication*, that this calls for an imaginative reconstruction of what he thinks, feels and sees in a situation. They go on to argue that this is not accomplished by magic, luck, or feeling good about the client. It is based on knowledge. This knowledge is gained by listening to the messages he sends, while at the same time being constantly aware of the things which influence how he sees the world: his values, culture, attitudes, etc. Information gained in this way can be used to formulate hypotheses about what the message means to the speaker. These hypotheses can then be tested against new information or they can be checked out by reflecting them back to the speaker.

Acceptance must not be confused with sympathy or agreement. Egan makes the point that sympathy, when aroused in the helper, can distort the stories she hears by blinding her to important nuances.

Acceptance means withholding judgement, especially in the early part of a conversation, neither agreeing nor disagreeing with what the client has said. It involves a readiness to understand the message from the other's point of view and communicating this readiness to the client by letting him know that what he has said has been both received and understood.

There are basically two types of reflective response: content responses and feeling responses.

Paraphrasing
Paraphrasing deals with facts and ideas rather than with emotions. Bolton defines a paraphrase as a concise response to the speaker which states the essence of his content in the listener's own words. The paraphrase can be distinguished from a detailed word-for-word summary (sometimes referred to as parroting) because it is brief, focused and is presented in the helper's own words, reflecting her understanding of the client's message.

Reflecting back feelings
Many helpers ignore the emotional dimension of a conversation and focus attention on the factual content of the message. Consider what this might mean in the context of an appraisal interview. By listening to the 'facts' a manager might built up an accurate picture about the quality of the work that her subordinate had been doing but, by filtering out the affective component of the message, might fail to appreciate that he finds his work very enjoyable and would be very unhappy with any change.

Bolton suggests a number of techniques the helper can use to become more aware of the affective component of a message. She can listen for 'feeling' words such as happy, sad, afraid, angry, surprised, disgusted; she can pay attention to the general content of the message and ask herself what she would be feeling; and she can observe body language. People often express their feelings without talking about them. A newly promoted employee who talks listlessly about his work and stares at the floor might not actually say that he is unhappy, but his non-verbal behaviour suggests that this might be the case. The skilled helper checks out her understanding (her hypothesis that he is unhappy) by reflecting back to the speaker the emotions he appears to be communicating.

Feeling and content can be reflected back together. The reflective responses offered by a helper who has used a listening framework similar to that proposed by Egan (see above) might involve the expression of core messages in terms of feelings, and the experiences and behaviours that underlie these feelings. After listening to the newly promoted employee the manager might reflect that:

> 'You feel unhappy about your promotion because you used to enjoy what you were doing and because you miss your friends.'

Carkhuff suggests, in *The Art of Helping*, that using a 'You feel ... because ...' format for reflective responses offers an easy and useful way of combining both feelings and fact.

Summative reflections

Bolton defines a summative reflection as a brief statement of the main themes and feelings that have been expressed by the client over a longer period of conversation than would be covered by the other two reflecting skills. In addition to providing the helper with an opportunity to check out her understanding of the overall message, summative reflections can help both the helper and the client develop a greater awareness of themes by tying together a number of separate comments. They can offer an especially useful way of helping the client appreciate the bigger picture. If, after listening for some time to what the client has to say, the helper summarises, and reflects back to him her understanding of his predicament by making a statement along the lines of:

> 'The problem doesn't just seem to be that you are unhappy about giving up the old job and losing contact with the people you used to work with. You also appear to be anxious and insecure in the new job because you think that you don't have what it takes to successfully supervise other "professionals".'

the client might begin to appreciate that there may be links which he had not previously considered and, as a result, may begin to think about his problem differently.

Summative reflections are also useful because they can reinforce positively the client's effort to communicate by providing direction to the conversation, creating a sense of movement and confirming that the helper is working hard to understand the client's message.

Summative reflections also offer a very useful way of restarting interrupted conversations.

> *Compare the reflecting skills discussed here with your responses to Exercises 6.1 and 6.2.*

In this chapter listening has been defined as the active search for a full and accurate understanding of the meaning of another's message. Some of the key skills which the helper can use to listen more effectively have been identified and elaborated. These skills have been considered under three headings: attending skills, which include the behaviours the helper needs to engage in to let the client know that she is paying careful attention to what he is saying; following skills; which include keeping the focus of attention on what the client has to say and encouraging him to tell his story; and reflecting skills, which provide the helper with the opportunity to check out her understanding and communicate this to the client and to help the client clarify his own thoughts.

Reflecting skills also assist the helper share with the client any themes she may have identified which could help the client appreciate the 'bigger picture' and develop a more objective understanding of his problem.

EXERCISE 6.5: PRACTISING EMPATHIC LISTENING

> This exercise involves a three-stage approach to practising empathic listening:
>
> 1 The first step involves observing what others do, and thinking about what they could do differently to become better empathic listeners. The aim of this step is to practise observing the skills presented in this chapter.
> 2 The second step involves using these observation skills to monitor and assess how you listen and to identify what you could do differently to improve your listening skill.
> 3 The third step involves taking action to improve the way you listen.

Step 1: Observing other people listening

Although it may not always be easy to observe people listening while they are helping, there will be many occasions when you will be able to observe people listening in the context of other relationships. You might have the opportunity of watching diners in a restaurant, a parent listening to what a child has to say or a shop assistant trying to understand the nature of a customer's complaint. Observe how people behave when they are listening.

Attending

Do they attend to the people they are listening to in ways that communicate to the speaker that they are interested in what he has to say? Use the **SOLER** mnemonic as a checklist:

S	Facing the speaker **S**quarely	Yes/No
O	Adopting an **O**pen posture	Yes/No
L	**L**eaning towards the speaker	Yes/No
E	Maintaining **E**ye contact	Yes/No
R	Appearing **R**elaxed	Yes/No

What could they do to improve their attending behaviour?

Following

How good are the listeners at getting the others to tell their story? Do they respond to cues offered by the speaker or use appropriate 'door openers' to get them talking? Do they manage to keep out of the speaker's way by using minimal prompts or accents to show the speaker that they are following what he is saying, or do they interrupt too often and/or ask too many of the kind of questions that divert the speaker away from the story he wants to tell? Note how often the listeners use:

- non-coercive invitations to talk (door openers)
- minimal prompts ('uh-huh', 'and ...?', 'tell me more')
- accents (one- or two-word re-statements)
- short statements
- infrequent questions for clarification
- attentive silences

> What could the listeners do differently that would communicate to the speaker that they are following what he is saying without, at the same time, interrupting his flow and getting in the way?

Reflecting

Do the listeners reflect back what they have heard to check that they have understood or to help the speaker clarify his thoughts or develop a better understanding of the bigger picture? Note how often the listeners use:

- paraphrasing
- reflecting back feelings
- summarising to draw the threads together and/or develop a bigger picture.

Could the listeners have adopted a better approach to checking out that they had understood the speaker, or to helping the speaker clarify his thoughts?

Step 2: Assessing your own approach to listening and identifying possible improvements

This stage involves opening a 'second channel' so that you can monitor your own listening behaviour by using your observation skills to observe yourself. It is important that you do not deliberately try to change your approach to listening at this point because the aim is to increase your awareness of your normal listening behaviour. Use the same approach to observing and assessing your own behaviour as you used in the first stage of this exercise to assess how other people listen.

Attending

Do *you* attend to others in ways that communicates that you are interested in what they have to say? Use the **SOLER** mnemonic as a checklist.

S	Facing the speaker **S**quarely	Yes/No
O	Adopting an **O**pen posture	Yes/No
L	**L**eaning towards the speaker	Yes/No
E	Maintaining **E**ye contact	Yes/No
R	Appearing **R**elaxed	Yes/No

What could you do to improve your attending behaviour?

Following

Do you make appropriate use of:

■ non-coercive invitations to talk (door openers)
■ minimal prompts ('uh-huh', 'and ...?', 'tell me more')
■ accents (one- or two-word re-statements)
■ short statements
■ infrequent questions for clarification
■ attentive silences?

What could you do differently that would communicate to the speaker that you are following what he is saying without, at the same time, interrupting his flow and getting in the way?

Reflecting

Do you reflect back what you have heard to check your understanding and/or help the speaker clarify his understanding? Do you make appropriate use of:

■   paraphrasing
■   reflecting back feelings
■   summarising to draw the threads together and/or develop a bigger picture?

Could you have adopted a better approach to checking that you fully understood what the speaker had to say and/or to helping the speaker clarify his thoughts?

Step 3: Taking action to improve your listening skills

This stage involves attending to those aspects of your own listening behaviour where you feel there is scope for improvement. If there are lots of changes that you feel you should make, you might think about whether you should try to introduce all of the changes at once or draw up a short list of a few changes to start with. You might, for example, decide to start by simply engaging in more eye contact and trying to use minimal prompts at some of the points in the conversation where you might normally have asked a question. Once these changes have been successfully introduced you might feel it appropriate to move on and introduce further changes.

Monitor the effects of these changes. Are you able to detect any differences in the way speakers respond to you? How do you feel about the new approach? When you apply these new listening skills in the helping relationship do they affect the way the client relates with you or the way he responds to his problem?

Make a note of the outcome of your efforts to improve your listening skills in the space provided below:

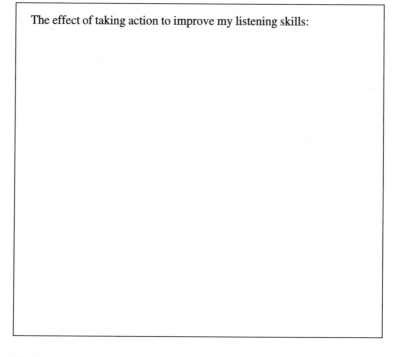

The effect of taking action to improve my listening skills:

If, the next time you look at this chapter, this box is still blank consider whether this is because you simply did not get round to recording the outcome or because you never made any attempt to improve your listening skills.

'Listening' to non-verbal behaviour

Listening involves more than simply paying attention to the spoken word. The rate at which words are spoken, the tone of voice used, and its pitch and volume can all convey meaning, as can the way the speaker is dressed, his gestures, eye contact and body movement. If the words are heard in isolation and the accompanying non-verbal signals, audio-vocal and visual-gestural, are ignored, then the helper may miss important information and her understanding of the client's message may be incomplete.

The majority of people find it easier to control the words they utter than to control the way they behave and the non-verbal signals they transmit. These non-verbal behaviours are often a source of 'leakage' through which people 'give off' signals about their emotional state, even when they are trying hard to hide their feelings. A dinner party guest sitting quietly with a sad expression on his face, or a student glaring across the lecture room with lowered brows, pressed lips and clenched fists are both 'giving off' information that could provide valuable information about their emotional states (such as loneliness, or anger) and interpersonal attitudes (such as being angry with a particular person).

If the helper is to be in a position to help the client develop a better understanding of his problem she needs to understand the problem as the client experiences it. This involves being aware of how he feels about the various aspects of the problem situation. It involves not only listening very carefully to what the client *says* about his feelings but also being alert to all the other information he 'gives off' about his true feelings.

Non-verbal signals can be a rich source of information. For a more detailed account read Chapter 3 in my book *Interpersonal Skills*. Observing and understanding them is as much a part of the process of effective listening as is listening to the spoken word.

Determining meaning

It is important to 'listen' to both verbal and non-verbal signals because, while there is often an overlap, words tend to emphasise factual content, whereas non-verbal signals emphasise the affective content of messages. Often these signals reinforce each other and communicate a consistent message. However, problems can arise when the words and the non-verbal signals appear to be sending contradictory messages. For example, what is the true meaning of the message if a red-faced man bangs the table with a clenched fist and declares in a loud voice that he is *not* angry? Research evidence suggests that the non-verbal behaviours will provide the most reliable clues to what the red-faced man is really feeling, in spite of the strong verbal statement that he is not angry.

There may also be occasions when different non-verbal signals give conflicting messages. Somebody 'smiles' with his lips but his body is tense and his fists are clenched. Here again there are research findings which suggest that certain of these signals are a more reliable indicator of feelings than others.

It appears that people are less likely to inhibit or manipulate certain signals. These tend to be those which they are the least aware of, believe others pay little attention to, or are beyond their control. Desmond Morris, in *Manwatching*, has proposed a 'Believability Scale' for different kinds of action. He suggests that autonomic signals are the most believable and verbalisations are the least believable. The seven elements in his scale are:

1   *Autonomic signals.* These include sweating, skin colour, respiratory patterns, etc. They are almost impossible to control because they result from physiological changes within the body. However, while they offer a very reliable indication of a person's emotional state, their occurrence tends to be limited to a relatively few dramatic situations. The body actions listed below tend to occur more frequently and therefore deserve special attention.

2   *Leg and foot signals.* People tend to focus most attention on the face, possibly because it is a highly expressive area. Even when it is possible to observe the whole body it is the face which receives most attention. It would appear that we normally pay least attention to those parts of the body which are farthest away from the face and, probably for the same reasons, we exert least deliberate control over these same parts of our own body. Since the feet are as far away from the face as you can get, it is not unreasonable to assume that they will provide valuable clues to a person's true mood. Foot actions which you might observe include aggressive toe jabs that may be at variance with friendly words and a smiling face, or restless and repetitive foot movements which suggest that the person is anxious to discontinue the interaction and get away. Moving on to consider the leg

as a whole, it may be possible to observe the soothing leg squeezing, where people cross their legs so that one limb feels the comforting pressure of the other, which suggests that a seemingly confident person is seeking some self-assurance, or flirtatious leg displays which conflict with upper-body primness.

3   *Trunk signals.* Posture can reflect the general muscular tonus of the whole body and therefore can be a useful guide to mood states. Somebody who is keyed up and excited will find it much more difficult to adopt a slumped posture than someone who is bored, unhappy or depressed.

4   *Unidentified gesticulations.* People tend to be more aware of hands, their own and others', than they are of feet. However, their awareness still tends to be relatively low, especially when the hands are used to make the vague and indefinite actions which accompany speech. Assertive finger wagging, imploring palm-up hand gestures, hand chops or hand rocking are some of the signals which can indicate what a person is really feeling. These 'illustrative gestures' are a better guide to the truth than the 'emblems' which are considered in the next category.

5   *Identified hand gestures.* We tend to be more aware of those hand gestures which are precise units of communication and which are deliberately performed. For this reason emblems such as the A-OK or the victory V signs cannot be trusted if they appear as part of a contradictory signal. A person might deliberately signal A-OK or thumbs up when he is feeling less than satisfied with his state of affairs. Consequently, such signals merit less weight than those discussed above.

6   *Facial expressions.* It is relatively easy to lie with the face. Most of us can fake anger or surprise with relative ease and therefore when contradictory signals are observed it might be best to ignore facial expressions. However, the careful observer might be able to see through many faked facial expressions and observe frozen smiles or other minute facial movements which provide clues to what the other is really feeling.

7   *Verbalisations.* As already mentioned, people are able to exercise most control over the verbal messages they give out. For this reason they are the least reliable guide to true feelings when contradictory signals are observed.

EXERCISE 6.6: IMPROVING YOUR ABILITY TO LISTEN TO NON-VERBAL SIGNALS

> Observe other people in conversation and ask yourself what they really feel about each other, about the issues being discussed and about themselves. Ask yourself such questions as 'who has the highest status?' and 'who is taking the lead in managing the interaction?' and pay careful attention to the sources of information you use to answer such questions.
>
> Think about the non-verbal behaviours you attend to when making your assessment and, bearing in mind Morris's 'Believability Scale', ask yourself whether you are paying sufficient attention to the most reliable signals.
>
> You might find it useful to start observing those signals which you tend to neglect and to monitor how the information you gain from attending to these previously neglected signals improves your ability better to understand the meaning of the messages you receive from other people.

One final point: remember that it can be dangerous to over-interpret the meaning of an isolated piece of behaviour. The art of effective listening to non-verbal messages is to recognise behaviours that may have potential message value and then to search for other behaviours which suggest a pattern. It is these patterns of behaviours, interpreted within context, which will enable you to determine the meaning of what you have seen and heard with a greater degree of confidence.

This chapter has been concerned with empathic listening. The next two chapters move on to consider how the helper can probe for information and can give feedback and challenge the client's view of himself and the problem situation. The use of these skills is not incompatible with empathic listening. In *Pragmatic Psychotherapy* Driscoll argues that empathic listening, which involves seeking to understand the client, can be a highly effective initial intervention which prepares the ground for more forceful strategies of change. The helper who has sought to understand the client and who acknowledges the client's position is more likely to be seen as an ally and is, therefore, in a better position to challenge the client's thinking.

7 Probing for information

Information gathering is an activity that we all engage in but the way we go about it will vary, depending on our purpose.

If the purpose is to obtain evidence from a suspect which might lead to a conviction, or to extract information from a terrorist that will reveal where he has planted a bomb and when it is timed to explode, the interviewer (interrogator) might feel justified in using a series of tactics that she might not normally use in other types of interaction. These could include the use of erratic sequences of questions designed to confuse and disorient the subject, thereby increasing the possibility that he will provide information that he would prefer to keep secret. The interrogator might also ask the kind of leading questions that exert pressure on the subject to answer in a particular way. The interrogator's purpose is to obtain the information she wants, not to collect information that will help the subject fulfil his own purpose.

Although she may go about it in a different way as compared with the interrogator, the selection interviewer is also striving to collect information that will serve her, rather than the candidates', purpose. She needs information that will help her decide which candidate is best for the post she is trying to fill.

The helper, on the other hand, collects information that will serve the client's, rather than her own, purpose. The aim of her information gathering is to help the client manage his own problems more effectively. This requires that she adopts a client-centred approach to probing for information.

THE AIMS OF INFORMATION GATHERING

It was noted in Chapter 4 that when a client tells his story he may present an incomplete or confusing picture and that the helper may have to press for more information and encourage the client to explore his problem situation more thoroughly and in more concrete terms. This additional information is required to help the client develop the level of understanding he will need if he is to manage the problem more effectively. Similar issues might arise when the client is describing what a more desirable state of affairs (an acceptable solution to his problem) would be like or when he is developing action plans to achieve this more desirable state. The helper might need to press the client to be more specific or to clarify his goals or plans.

EXERCISE 7.1: PROBING FOR INFORMATION, PART 1

Think of a recent occasion when you tried to help somebody. Even though you may not be able to recall everything that was said, write the best account you can of the interaction (or of a significant part of it) in the style of a script:

What I said
What he said, etc.

Try to remember what you said and record it in as much detail as possible. If you cannot remember precisely what you said write down what you think you probably would have said and the questions you would have asked. The aim of this part of the exercise is to provide an indication of the kinds of intervention you think you typically use. It does not have to be a word-perfect record. You will be asked to refer back to this account at the end of the chapter.

continued

Exercise 7.1, part 1, *continued*

Exercise 7.1, part 1, *continued*

The helper may try to help the client by probing for information in order to:

1   *Seek clarification when the helper has not fully understood what the client has said.* It was mentioned in Chapter 3 that empathic listening involves the helper understanding the client's problem from within his (the client's) frame of reference and communicating this understanding to him. If the helper feigns understanding this could undermine later helping interventions. For example, if the helper attempts to challenge the client's thinking on a particular issue and if this challenge is based on a misunderstanding of the client's position, that could undermine the helper's credibility. When the helper is confused, or if she has not heard what the client has said, she needs to be honest about it and seek clarification.

'I'm not sure that I have understood your last point, could you go over it again?'

2   *Move the client away from thinking in terms of vague generalities towards more concrete specifics.* Unless the client begins to think about his problems in concrete, operational terms it will be difficult for him to develop an effective approach to managing his problems for himself. The example (in Chapter 3) of the manager who complained that the quality of his working life was deteriorating illustrates how it is possible to move a client from a vague statement of the problem to one which focuses on a number of specific issues. The initial clarification probe might have been a very open question such as:

'What exactly do you mean when you say that the quality of your working life is deteriorating?'

As the helper listens to what the manager has to say she may attempt to focus his thinking even further by asking him to justify his statements:

'Why did you say that?'

Or she might invite him to illustrate his point with an example which could provide a more concrete statement of the problem:

'You say that you spend too much time away from the office.

Can you give me an example of the problems this can lead to?'

3   *Draw the client's attention to aspects of the situation he might be unaware of or is choosing to ignore.* Questions can prompt the client to think differently about why a problem might have arisen or about ways it could be managed more effectively. A colleague may have described a destructive conflict which is damaging the performance of his work group and explained, at great length, how it is being fuelled by the way Jim, one of his subordinates, refuses to do what he is told and encourages others to accept his view of how things should be done. The helper may have noticed that at no point did the colleague consider how his own actions may be contributing to the situation. In order to encourage the colleague to view the problem from an alternative perspective the helper might ask:

'Have you considered the situation from Jim's perspective? If he were telling me about the problem what might he say?'

The helper might also encourage the client to question his assumptions by adopting an approach which has already been mentioned above as an aid to facilitating more concrete thinking. She might ask him to justify his position:

'Why do you believe that?'

'Is there any evidence to justify your assumption that . . .?'

Challenging the client is considered in more detail in the next chapter.

4   *Move the client to the next stage of managing his problem.* Asking questions can shift the client's attention to what has to be done next to manage his problem. He might have developed a very good understanding of his problem but does not seem to be using this new awareness to improve matters. The helper might feel that the client needs to be encouraged to think about what a more desirable scenario would look like:

'Now that you have a better idea of what is wrong with your present job, can you tell me what your ideal job would look like?'

In a similar way, as the client begins to take action to achieve a desired goal the helper might prompt him to begin thinking about how he will consolidate the change:

'What kind of things will you have to attend to if all this effort is not to be wasted, so you don't end up back where you started?'

5   *Help the client identify themes and see the 'bigger picture'.* The skilled listener can often identify potential links and relationships that the client misses because he is too involved with the detail of his problem. The client may be behaving in accordance with the old adage and concentrating so much attention on the detail (the trees) that he fails to see how the details form part of a wider whole (the wood). One way of drawing the bigger picture to the client's attention (already mentioned in Chapter 6) is to offer him a 'summative reflection' which provides a brief statement of the main themes he has referred to. Another approach is to invite the client to consider and explain the possible relationship between ideas, people, events, etc.:

'Does this relate to what you said earlier about . . .?'

AVOID ASKING TOO MANY QUESTIONS

It was noted in Chapter 6 that many helpers make an excessive and inappropriate use of questions. The over-use of questions can give the client the impression that he is being interrogated and can interrupt his flow. Questions need to be used sparingly and asked with a clear purpose in mind. It is all too easy to ask a question (any question) simply because there is a pause and the helper does not know what she should do next. So she asks a question. In such circumstances the helper might have been more effective if, rather than asking a question, she had employed any of the other 'following behaviours' mentioned in Chapter 6.

If the client is bombarded with questions he may be pushed into a reactive mode, providing the information he is asked for but failing to think out for himself what information he requires. Helper interventions that provoke this kind of response are not helpful. They do nothing to assist others to become more proactive in the management of their own problems. Clients can be encouraged to become more proactive by being prompted to identify and ask relevant questions for themselves. The helper might achieve this by asking questions along the following lines:

'What are some of the important questions you need to ask yourself if . . . (you are going to push ahead and allocate more time to the new project and delegate more responsibility to the area sales managers)?'

DIFFERENT KINDS OF QUESTIONS

Sometimes the reason why the helper gets locked into asking too many questions is because the type of question she asks fails to encourage the client to tell his story. It may be the type of question that requires a very brief answer and once this has been provided the helper is confronted with a silence – which she fills with another question of the same type. The type of question that often elicits this kind of brief response is a closed question.

Closed questions

Closed questions are those which require the respondent to reply by selecting a response from a series of pre-determined categories offered by the interviewer. There are three main types of closed question. The most common is where the respondent is offered the two categories Yes and No, for example:

'Are you over 21?'

There is usually a correct answer to this kind of question and therefore it can be an effective way of obtaining specific information quickly. At the scene of an accident a supervisor might ask an operator:

Supervisor: 'Are you hurt?'
Operator: 'Yes.'

Until she has established this she may not be able to decide whether the operator requires any help to manage the incident, and if he does what kind of help might be most useful.

Another kind of closed question, sometimes referred to as the identification question, requires the respondent to identify and offer a correct factual response, for example:

Supervisor: 'What time did the accident happen?'
Operator: 'Six o'clock.'

The third kind of closed question offers the respondent a range of alternative answers from which he is required to select the one which best approximates to his own opinion. This form of question is sometimes referred to as a forced-choice question, for example:

'Immediately before the accident where was the temperature indicator, at blue, green or red?'

Where blue, green and red are the only alternatives the correct answer is easy to select but, if the temperature gauge included intermediate colours, none of the possibilities offered may provide an ideal answer. If the indicator had been in the orange zone but had been rising quickly towards the red, the operator may have selected red as the best of the available options.

Closed questions tend to be easier to answer than open questions and therefore can be useful icebreakers at the start of a conversation:

'Can I take your coat?'

'Would you like some coffee?'

They also enable the helper to exercise control and focus the client's attention on relevant issues. This can be very useful in some situations. In a non-helping situation, for example, a customs officer may not be interested in whether a returning holiday-maker has enjoyed his holiday or whether his flight was delayed. However, in order for her to achieve her own aim, she may want to know whether he is aware of the duty-free allowances, how many cigarettes or bottles of wine and spirit he has and whether he is importing goods over a specified value. A series of closed questions will enable her to elicit this information, and only this information. For example:

Officer: 'Are you aware of the duty-free allowance?'   (a yes–
              no question)

Traveller: 'Yes.'
Officer: 'How many cigarettes do you have?' (an identification question)
Traveller: 'Two hundred.'

However, closed questions may be less effective in the helping relationship because in some circumstances they deny the client the opportunity to say what he wants to say.

It is also possible that where a helper asks questions that invite simple yes or no answers she may fail to learn why the client answered the way he did. After spending some time working with one of her section leaders to help him improve the performance of his section a manager/helper might enquire:

'Did you meet the delivery targets for Uniflex UK last week?'

The answer:

'Yes.'

may mislead the manager into thinking that the section had achieved this performance target because the section leader was managing his section more effectively, whereas the real reason may have been that another customer had cancelled an order, thus freeing output that could be diverted to the Uniflex UK order. A more open question such as:

'How did the section perform last week?'

might have provided more useful information which the manager/helper could use to assess how the section leader had been managing the situation.

Open questions

Open questions do not restrict the respondent to answering within a framework of a pre-determined set of categories. Respondents are left free to reply in their own words and to answer the question in any way they like. Compare the closed question:

'Do you like your new job?'

with the open question:

'What do you think of your new job?'

The closed question may only elicit a yes–no reply whereas the open question is likely to provide not only information about the respondent's affective response to his job, but also some explanation of why he feels the way he does.

Open questions that make use of Kipling's six honest serving men (who taught him all he knew – their names were What and Why and When and How and Where and Who) encourage the respondent to talk. 'Yes' would not be an adequate reply to the question:

'What do you think of your new job?'

Open questions can also produce answers that the helper may never have expected and therefore provide access to information that would not have been revealed by the replies to a series of closed questions. For example, a manager who knows that a member of her team had been dreading a recent reorganisation and the introduction of a new management information system might have asked him:

Manager: 'What do you think of your new job now?'
Subordinate: 'It's better than I expected. The possibility of using a modem for remote working from home means that I could buy a house in the Dales and work from there. We have always planned to move when I retire but now we don't have to wait.'

The reply to this open-ended question might have provided more information about his motives than a more focused question such as:

'Has the new job presented you with any special problems?'

It must be remembered, however, that the helper is not simply presented with the stark choice of asking either an open or a closed question. The degree of openness, and therefore the degree of control that the helper can exercise over the way the client will reply, can be varied by the helper. Compare:

'How are things?'

'How are things at work?'

'How are you getting on with your new assistant?'

'How are you managing your new assistant's negative attitude towards working for a woman?'

These are all open questions, but some are more focused than others and impose more restrictions on the way the client can answer.

Leading questions

Leading questions are questions that lead the client to provide a certain kind of answer:

'You are not going to let her get away with that, are you?'

It is obvious from the way the question was phrased that the 'helper' expects the client to say no. While leading questions can play a useful role in some forms of social interaction (for example in the courtroom where a barrister is trying to secure a conviction) they are less useful in the helping relationship. They can undermine the client's willingness to be open and honest and encourage him to provide the answers that he thinks the helper wants to hear. It is important, therefore, that the helper exercises care to avoid signalling a preferred response when asking questions. Leading questions are incompatible with empathic listening where the aim is to understand the client's problem from within his own frame of reference.

EXERCISE 7.1, PART 2

Refer back to the account you wrote at the beginning of this chapter.

1   Examine the nature of your interventions. Were all of your interventions questions? Did you make sufficient and/or appropriate use of other interventions such as minimal prompts, accents, statements, summative reflections, etc.? (See Chapter 6 for details.)

2   Look at each of the questions you asked and consider why you asked it. Did your reason correspond to one of the five purposes for collecting information listed above? What other reasons motivated you to ask questions? Were these reasons compatible with the approach to helping advocated in this book?

3   What kind of questions did you ask (open, closed or leading)? Did you make sufficient use of open questions? If you asked closed or leading questions was their use justified?

Next time you are engaged in helping somebody, observe your own behaviour and monitor your approach to collecting information.

EXERCISE 7.2: LISTENING TO YOUR OWN QUESTIONS

Now that you have given some thought to the kinds of question you ask and your purpose for asking questions, open a 'second channel' so that you can stand outside yourself and monitor your own behaviour as it unfolds during an actual helping episode.

As soon as possible make some time to consider how helpful your questioning was. Is there any room for improvement? If so, what changes might be called for?

8 *Offering feedback and challenging assumptions*

Helping involves both supporting and challenging others in their struggle to manage their problems more effectively.

Feedback can be a source of support *and* challenge. It can be a source of support when the helper acknowledges the effort the client has invested in trying to manage his problem more effectively and when she confirms that his effort is leading to progress. It can be a source of challenge when it presents the client with new information that may require him to reconsider the nature of his problem, that questions the effectiveness of his efforts to resolve it or that even contests his commitment to securing any improvement.

A client's ability to manage his own problems can be fettered by limited or incorrect perceptions, especially about himself and his relations with others. Feedback which offers clients new information about themselves can help them develop alternative perspectives on problems. The Johari window is a model developed by Joseph Luft and Harry Ingham, two American psychologists, which can be used to illustrate the process of giving feedback in the helping relationship. An adaptation of this model is shown in Figure 8.1. The client's view of himself is represented by the vertical columns in the figure and the helper's view of the client by the horizontal rows.

Nobody knows everything about themselves. What they know is represented by the left-hand column. The upper pane, referred to as the *open area*, depicts that knowledge about the self that the client is either willing to or cannot avoid sharing with others, including the helper. The lower pane, referred to as the *façade* or hidden area, depicts that knowledge about himself that the client would prefer not

CLIENT'S VIEW OF SELF

		Things client knows about self	Things client does not know
HELPER'S VIEW OF CLIENT	Things the helper knows about the client	OPEN OR SHARED AREA	BLIND SPOT
	Things the helper does not know about client	FAÇADE OR HIDDEN AREA	UNKNOWN

Figure 8.1   The helping relationship (Johari window)

to share and therefore attempts to keep hidden from the helper. As respect and trust develop between helper and client the client may be willing to reveal more of what he initially attempted to keep hidden. Façades are dropped and real concerns discussed more openly. In terms of the Johari window, the client begins to behave in ways which increase the open area and reduce the hidden area.

What the client does not know about himself is represented by the right-hand column. This column contains two panes, the blind spot and the unknown, which will be discussed in more detail below.

What the helper knows or does not know about the client is represented by the rows. The bottom row depicts what the helper does not know about the client. The bottom left-hand pane (the façade or hidden area) can be reduced only when the client decides to share more information with the helper. However, the helper can facilitate this process by behaving towards the client in ways which help him tell his story. All the relationship-building and exploring and clarifying skills that are referred to in earlier chapters can help achieve this end. The bottom right-hand pane, the *unknown*, depicts knowledge that has not yet been discovered by either client or helper. A supportive relationship in which the helper shows empathy towards the client can sometimes enable the client to access information, such as previously repressed emotional reactions, that can help him better understand the issues he is trying to deal with.

The top row of the Johari window represents what the helper knows about the client. The top left-hand pane, already referred to, depicts that knowledge which is shared by helper and client. The top right-hand pane, the *blind spot*, depicts information which the helper knows about the client but which the client does not know about himself. The helper may have obtained this information in a number of ways: by observing the client's behaviour; by paying careful attention to all he says; by searching for and identifying underlying themes; and, sometimes, by reference to external sources of data such as reports from customers, colleagues, etc. By offering feedback the helper is disclosing to the client information about himself that he might otherwise not have access to. In other words, she is revealing to the client information about his blind spots.

FEEDBACK AND SELF-DISCLOSURE IN THE HELPING RELATIONSHIP

The Johari window provides a useful model for exploring some aspects of client and helper behaviour.

Client behaviour

The helping relationship involves the client telling his story. This is the focus of the 'inward journey' (in the early stages of the helping relationship) and involves the client lowering his façade and disclosing his private thoughts to the helper. At a later stage in the helping relationship (starting with the outward journey) the client also needs to be receptive to and to seek feedback from the helper and others in order to reduce his blind spots. As the relationship develops some clients actively engage in both of these aspects of client behaviour whereas others favour one more than the other, or are reluctant to engage in either. Four types of client that a helper may encounter are discussed below.

The open and receptive client

Where the client engages in both of these kinds of activity, disclosing information and soliciting and being receptive to feedback, his behaviour is shown in Figure 8.2. He lowers his façade and is open with the helper about his real concerns, and he recognises the importance of exploring his blind spots. This involves being prepared

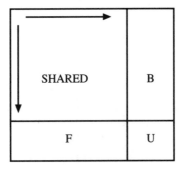

Figure 8.2   The open and receptive client. B, U and F are respectively blind spot, unknown and façade, as in Figure 8.1

to adopt a non-defensive response to the feedback he is offered and soliciting additional feedback where he feels others might have information that could be helpful.

The telling client
The helper may encounter some clients who are willing, may be even eager, to tell their story but who are much less interested in or receptive to any feedback that may be available. This kind of client may actively seek out people who are willing to listen. Figure 8.3 illustrates an extreme example of this kind of *'telling* client'. He may derive considerable benefit from the opportunity to tell his story. The helper's willingness to listen may provide an opportunity for him to discharge some of the emotions that are clouding his thinking or may simply encourage him to think through his problem in a more constructive way. In such circumstances the client may not require any further help. However, there are clients who are willing to present their problem, maybe to seek sympathy, but who are not really interested in anything that contradicts their definition of the problem or challenges their proposed strategy for responding (or not responding) to the situation. They find it difficult to let go of their subjective view and are closed to information that might help them explore the problem from a different perspective. They are unwilling to face up to the challenge that feedback may present. Later in this chapter some consideration will be given to ways of providing feedback and presenting challenges that might be more acceptable to such clients.

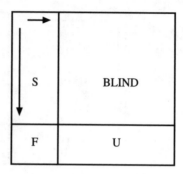

Figure 8.3   The telling client

The soliciting client

A third type of a client is the person who appears eager to solicit others' views but is unwilling to disclose much information about himself and keeps his thoughts hidden from the helper. This *soliciting* client is illustrated in Figure 8.4. Clients may behave in this way for a number of reasons. For example, they may feel competent to manage their own problem but recognise the need for external data against which to test their assessment of the situation and their chosen approach to problem management. In such circumstances the helper might not need to be too concerned about such a client's lack of openness so long as she is confident that he is using the feedback constructively. However, this may not always be the case and the helper may suspect that the client is not receptive to feedback and is

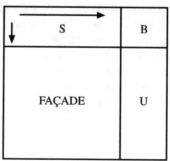

Figure 8.4   The soliciting client

not managing his problem effectively. The client may only be seeking feedback in order to create the impression that he is open to alternative points of view. This kind of difficulty frequently arises in the workplace where the helper is the client's boss and where the client feels under pressure to listen to his boss.

There are also clients, in a variety of work and non-work situations, who may feel less inhibited about soliciting or listening to feedback than sharing information about themselves. This is because they feel able to do so without admitting a weakness, failure or inadequacy. When they receive feedback that might be challenging they may reject it or at least refuse to discuss it, thereby protecting their self-esteem. Sharing information about themselves means that they have to lower their façade and expose themselves to others. This might involve confronting weaknesses or inade- quacies that they would prefer to hide – from themselves as well as from others.

In these circumstances the helper needs to pay careful attention to relationship building in order to develop the trust and confidence that will encourage the client to share more information and to 'use' the helper to help him develop a more objective view of himself and his problem situation. The helper also needs to pay very careful attention to the client's non-verbal behaviour for indications of his reaction to any feedback she does offer, and she needs to consider how far she should go in responding to the client's desire for feedback when he is unwilling to discuss his problem or respond in any meaningful way to the information she provides.

The helper also needs to be particularly wary in those circum- stances where the client is reluctant to share information about himself but solicits feedback and *advice* about what he should do. Even if the helper is tempted to offer advice, how useful can it be if it is not based on a thorough understanding of the problem situation? If the client refuses to disclose information the helper is denied this understanding. Except in very special circumstances, such as an emergency which threatens the client's ability to manage his own problems in the future, the provision of such advice is unlikely to have any long-term beneficial effects and, as mentioned on a number of occasions, may make the client more rather than less dependent on the helper.

The reluctant client

The fourth type of client has been labelled *reluctant* and his behaviour is illustrated in Figure 8.5. Not only is he reluctant to engage in self-disclosure but he is also closed to feedback for all the reasons considered above.

A number of writers have made a clear distinction between reluctant and resistant clients. They use the term 'resistance' to refer to the reaction of clients who feel coerced in some way: it is the passive or active opposition to external pressure. Resistant clients may not believe that they have a problem or, if they do, they may reject the need for external help. Help may be rejected because they fear that it will make them dependent on another person, or it may be rejected because they do not want to admit to a weakness or inadequacy. Reluctance, on the other hand, is a term that is often used to refer to the ambiguity a client feels when he realises that managing his problem more effectively is going to exact a price that he is not certain he wants to pay. Whereas resistant clients may refuse to engage in the helping process, reluctant clients may participate but they may be prepared to respond only to non-threatening feedback or to share limited information and discuss only low-risk problems. Reluctant clients may be more likely to test the helper by presenting a low-risk problem before deciding whether to share the problem that is really bothering them. While it is recognised here that the distinction between resistance and reluctance can be important, the reactions they describe have been grouped together under the generic heading of reluctance.

It is possible for the helper to take a number of steps that might

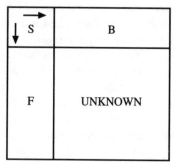

Figure 8.5   The reluctant client

minimise this reluctance. The helper can start by helping the client consider whether there is a need for change and avoid starting from the premise that the client does have a problem. The client may have made an assessment, on the information available to him, that led him to the conclusion that there is no problem and therefore no reason why things cannot continue as before. This assessment may be correct. In an article in the *Harvard Business Review*, Kotter and Schlesinger warn of the danger of managers (helpers) arriving at a different assessment and becoming impatient with those who do not share their view of the need for change. Such helpers see resistance as bad and therefore fight it. Resistance needs to be seen by the helper in more neutral terms (rather than inherently bad) and as something which is normal and to be expected. Egan, in *The Skilled Helper*, suggests that it can also be useful if the client can be helped to see that he is not odd because he is reluctant or resistant. It is also possible that the helper may feel hurt by a client's rejection of her offer of help. Many of these reactions of both clients and helpers can be avoided if the helper accepts the client's frame of reference as the starting point and behaves towards him in ways that demonstrate her respect for his point of view. (See the discussion of respect in Chapter 5.)

Helper behaviour

The helping relationship involves the helper relating with the client in a number of ways. She seeks information by soliciting feedback from the client about how well she has understood his problem and about how effective her interventions have been. This activity has the effect of moving the vertical line in Figure 8.6 to the right. She also provides the client with information by giving him feedback and challenging his subjective view of himself and his problem situation, and by engaging in appropriate self-disclosure of her own experiences, actions and feelings where they might be of help to the client. These actions push the horizontal line in Figure 8.6 down.

Soliciting feedback to check how well the helper has understood the client's problem has been discussed in Chapter 6, 'Listening', under the heading 'Reflecting'. Attending to non-verbal behaviour can also be a rich source of information about the client's reaction to the helper's other interventions.

Just as the Johari window provides a framework for categorising clients on the basis of their information-seeking and information-

Soliciting feedback on the effectiveness of
helper interventions and understanding of
client's problem

Providing feedback and
challenging the client, and
disclosing information about self

S	B
F	U

Figure 8.6   Helper behaviour

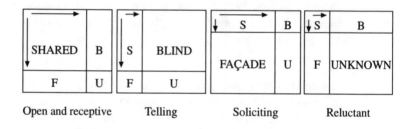

SHARED	B	S	BLIND
F	U	F	U

Open and receptive   Telling

S	B	S	B
FAÇADE	U	F	UNKNOWN

Soliciting   Reluctant

Figure 8.7   Four types of helper

giving behaviour, so it also provides a framework for categorising
helpers on the same basis. Four types of helper are presented in
Figure 8.7.

The *open and receptive helper* is both an active seeker and
provider of information. She monitors her own effectiveness as a
helper and even with reluctant or soliciting clients she works hard to
obtain feedback. She is also open and honest with the people she
relates with. She is prepared to let them know how she feels about
them and to provide them with constructive feedback that will help
them develop an effective approach to problem management. Above

all, she is not afraid to confront and challenge others and has the skill to do this effectively. She is also willing to disclose information about herself if she feels this will help the client.

The *telling helper* may have a tendency to behave like the proverbial bull in a china shop. She may spend too much of the time talking and because she fails to seek feedback on her own effectiveness she may not have fully understood what the client has said and she may be unaware of how her other interventions, including the giving of feedback, challenging and self-disclosing, have been received, and whether or not they have helped.

The *soliciting helper* may be so concerned with empathising with the client and soliciting feedback to reassure herself that she has understood what he has said that she gets locked into the early stages of the helping process and fails to recognise when it is time to move on. She may also be so concerned to win the approval of the client that she is over-sensitive to how he reacts to her interventions. This might make her reluctant to challenge him and offer any feedback that may disturb his view of things, thereby avoiding the possibility that she might threaten his positive regard for her. The effective helper needs to seek feedback to assess her own effectiveness but she needs to have the self-assurance not to base this assessment solely on whether the client finds her interventions comfortable. Some very effective interventions might be effective because of the discomfort they produce. It may be this which provides the client with the motivation to change.

The *reluctant helper*, like the reluctant client, may be someone who would rather not have to bother and would prefer to be doing something else. Therefore she fails to engage in the behaviours necessary to solicit or provide the information that is so essential if the helper's interventions are to be successful. However, the problem may not be motivation. The helper may not appreciate what is required of her or it may be that she lacks the confidence or skill to intervene and act like the open and receptive helper she would like to be.

The next three sections will consider some of the helper behaviours that involve the helper sharing information with the client: giving feedback, challenging and self-disclosure.

Giving helpful feedback

Not all feedback is helpful. Poor feedback can damage the helping relationship and result in the client being less open to further feedback and more reluctant to share information with the helper. In other words, it can reduce the size of the open or shared area in the client's Johari window and can undermine the client's confidence in his own ability to manage problems effectively. While poor feedback can damage the helping relationship, the provision of high-quality feedback can be very helpful. It can be a valuable source of support and an important motivator that can play a key role in maintaining the client's commitment. It can also draw the client's attention to aspects of his own behaviour or the problem situation that have been neglected and can challenge his subjective assessment and encourage him to consider alternative ways of framing his problem or evaluating the effects of his behaviour.

What follows is a set of widely accepted guidelines for the provision of helpful feedback.

1   *Helpful feedback is descriptive, not judgmental.* To be told:

> 'You are an arrogant bully.'

is less helpful than to be informed that:

> 'Whenever you and I discuss this kind of issue I am left with the feeling that you don't listen to my views and that you attempt to get your way by threatening me.'

The first example is evaluative: the helper is making a judgement about the client's behaviour. The second example is more descriptive. It describes the effect the client's behaviour has on the helper, which might be precisely the effect the client wants. He might have decided that the best way to influence the helper is to issue threats. However, this may not be his intention and the feedback may alert the client to important unanticipated consequences of his behaviour.

2   *Helpful feedback is specific, not general.* To be told:

> 'You never seem to be able to communicate effectively in groups.'

offers the client few clues about what he might do differently to improve matters. On the other hand, to be told that:

'When you were presenting your case to the group last Thursday you spoke so quickly that I couldn't grasp all the points you were trying to make.'

provides the client with information which is sufficiently specific for him to determine how he might change his behaviour if he wants to obtain a different outcome at the next meeting.

3 *Helpful feedback is relevant to the needs of the client.* The helper needs to be aware of whose needs she is trying to satisfy when she offers feedback. Sometimes feedback does more for the helper than the client. For example, an angry outburst may help relieve her frustrations but do little for the client. Similarly, the provision of sensitive feedback in public may do more to confirm the helper's superiority than to boost the confidence of the client who may be a new member of the helper's work group.

4 *Helpful feedback is solicited rather than imposed.* In many circumstances people seek feedback. However, while they want to know they may be fearful of finding out. The helper needs to be sensitive to those cues which indicate whether the other person is seeking feedback and to those cues which signal when he has received as much as he can cope with for the time being. Pushing too hard can trigger a defensive reaction, leading the client to dismiss or ignore further feedback. People tend to be much less receptive to feedback which they feel is imposed than to that which they have sought out for themselves.

5 *Helpful feedback is timely and in context.* Feedback is best given in the context in which the behaviour to which the feedback refers took place, and as soon after the behaviour as possible. The introduction of formalised appraisal systems sometimes encourage helpers to store up feedback for the appraisal interview when it would have been much more effective if it had been offered at the time the problem was observed by the helper. However, accurate behavioural records, on audio or video tape, for example, can extend considerably the period over which the feedback is timely; these methods also preserve much of the context and therefore are particularly valuable in training situations.

6 *Helpful feedback is usable and concerned with behaviour over which the client is able to exercise control.* Feedback can improve the client's knowledge of how he typically behaves and

the effect his behaviour has on others. However, feedback can help the client secure desired outcomes only if it focuses on behaviour he can do something about. To tell a client with a severe stutter that he is making you impatient, and that he should be quick and say what he has to say or shut up, is unlikely to afford much help.

7   *Feedback can be helpful only when it has been heard and understood.* If in doubt check with the client to ensure that the feedback has been received and understood.

EXERCISE 8.1: ASSESSING THE QUALITY OF FEEDBACK

This is a three-stage exercise. First, using the checklist provided below, observe others when they are giving feedback (parents providing feedback to their children, a football coach giving feedback to members of his team, a manager giving feedback to her subordinate or the subordinate giving feedback to the manager) and assess whether their feedback complies with the guidelines presented above. Note which of the seven guidelines are most frequently neglected and observe, as best you can, the recipients' reaction to the feedback they receive and whether their reaction is related to the way in which it is presented.

Note whether the feedback is:

Descriptive	. . . .	Judgemental
Specific	. . . .	General
Relevant to client's needs	. . . .	Irrelevant to client's needs
Focused on behaviour client can control	. . . .	Focused on behaviour client cannot control
Solicited	. . . .	Imposed
Timely	. . . .	Delayed
Checked for understanding	. . . .	Not checked for understanding

Next, open a 'second channel' and monitor yourself when you give feedback.
Do you follow the guidelines?

To what extent do frustration and anger influence the quality of your feedback?

Are there certain situations or relationships where you take less care over the feedback you give to others?

Can you identify ways of improving the quality of the feedback you give to others?

Finally, in the space provided below, note the actions you could take to improve the quality of the feedback you give to others.

Find an early opportunity to implement these changes and monitor the effect they have on the recipient of your feedback.

Challenging

The goal of challenging or confronting in the helping relationship is to help clients explore those areas of experience, feeling and behaviour which they have so far failed to explore. In their book *Consultation*, Blake and Mouton suggest that confrontational interventions can be among the most effective in reducing the efficacy of defence mechanisms. By challenging the client, the helper can persuade him to face up to contradictions between what he says and does or between how he sees himself and the way others see him. The helper might also challenge the client because she suspects that he distorts reality and uses these distortions to avoid facing up to things. For example, a client might view his subordinate's application for a better job as disloyalty rather than as a timely and appropriate career move, or he may disguise (even from himself) his fear of change as a commitment to the one best and traditional way of doing things.

Egan, in *The Skilled Helper*, suggests that, in its simplest form, a confrontation is an invitation to examine some form of behaviour that seems to be self-defeating, harmful or both and to change that behaviour if it is found to be so. As mentioned in Chapter 1, confrontation is strong medicine that can be destructive in the hands of the inept. Effective challenges are never punitive accusations. They are invitations to explore contradictions and distortions, or invitations to identify and employ unused strengths and resources. Egan argues that the term 'invitation' cannot be emphasised too strongly. The client who experiences the challenge as a shameful unmasking or some other form of attack will not be receptive to the alternative perspective that the challenge may offer. A likely outcome is that the client who feels under attack will direct his energy towards a defensive action and possibly a counter-attack aimed at discrediting the 'helper'. Consider how you might react to the following challenges:

(a) 'Why don't you start being honest? You feel so damned sorry for yourself most of the time that you never even give a thought to the possibility that you might be the cause of most of your own problems. You mope around and never face up to things. Grow up!!'

(b) 'Let me check something out with you. You say that you have been feeling very low because everything seems to be going wrong. You also indicate that there is nothing you can do to change things. Now, I'm not sure about this. From what I've observed you appear to behave as if you believe that you can't change things and therefore you don't even try, even in circumstances when you could. For example, you didn't even try to make a case for an increase to your budget at the last managers' meeting. You seem to blame others for your problems but do nothing to change things. Does this make sense to you?'

The second challenge was based on what the client had said and on what the helper had observed. It started by acknowledging the client's point of view, thus signalling that he was understood and that the helper was 'with' rather than against him. It was specific and offered examples. It was also presented tentatively. The phrases 'I'm not sure about this' and 'does this make sense to you?' offered the client the options of accepting, modifying or even rejecting the confrontation without feeling accused by the helper.

Helpful challenges are those which encourage the client to seek greater self-understanding. As well as being based on accurate empathy and presented tentatively they must also be made when the client is in a fit state to respond. To paraphrase Egan, a confused and disorganised client might be further disoriented by a challenge which adds to his confusion.

EXERCISE 8.2: CHALLENGING

> Think of the people who have been most and least effective in their attempts to challenge your thinking and behaviour. Try to recollect the nature of their challenges and attempt to identify what it was that differentiated those that were successful from those that were not. Review your answers using Table 8.1.

When you next feel the need to confront somebody, open a 'second channel' and monitor your own challenging behaviour. Note how it relates to the guidelines presented in Table 8.1 and consider whether you are able to identify areas for improvement. If you are, make a note of them in the space provided below the table.

Table 8.1   Characteristics of successful and unsuccessful challenges

Nature of challenge	Most successful challenges	Least successful challenges
1 Based on accurate empathy?	Yes/No	Yes/No
2 Specific (illustrated with relevant examples)?	Yes/No	Yes/No
3 Offered tentatively (providing the opportunity for discussion, even rejection)?	Yes/No	Yes/No
4 Made in circumstances where you were unlikely to feel humiliated and defensive?	Yes/No	Yes/No
5 Other (specify)	Yes/No	Yes/No
6 Other (specify)	Yes/No	Yes/No

Areas for improvement

Helper self-disclosure

Egan advocates appropriate self-disclosure and believes that the helper should be willing to disclose himself to the client when he feels it will be useful and when it will contribute to the achievement of a counselling/helping goal. He supports its use when it helps the client focus more clearly, and think more concretely and accurately about his areas of ineffectiveness and about the resources he can draw upon to be more effective.

Helper self-disclosure, like feedback, can be a source of support and yet be challenging to the client. On the one hand it can reassure him that he is not alone and that others have been where he is and have survived and even thrived. On the other hand it can increase the pressure on the client to reveal himself. In his book *The Transparent Self*, Sidney Jourard refers to this as disclosure reciprocity and argues that it can both increase the amount and improve the quality of client self-disclosure. When one person (the helper) discloses personal information this tends to produce a feeling of liking and trust in the other person (the client). If the helper's self-disclosure is focused on issues that relate to important aspects of the client's problem it might encourage him to respond by sharing more information about his problem and to present it in a more detailed and concrete way.

Egan suggests that helper self-disclosure can increase the helper's power base and her ability to influence the client because it:

(a) increases the helper's attractiveness to the client;
(b) enhances the helper's trustworthiness because she has demonstrated to the client that she trusts him enough to reveal herself;
(c) makes the helper's attempts to empathise with the client more credible because she is able to demonstrate that she has shared similar experiences. For example, often the people who are able to offer addicts the most effective help are those who have been addicts themselves.

There is, however, some evidence that helper self-disclosure is not always helpful. Some clients may be frightened by the level of intimacy that the helping process seems to demand. Instead of encouraging them to reveal more about themselves it might have the opposite effect and result in the client distancing himself from the helper.

If it is to be effective, helper self-disclosure should be used sparingly and selectively and it should not be used in ways that undermine helping goals. For example, it should not be used if it will add yet another burden to an already overburdened client:

'I know how you feel. My wife left me three weeks ago. I had no idea it was going to happen. It's been terrible . . .'

Helper self-disclosure is unhelpful if it distracts the client from working on his own problem. He should not be made to feel that he needs to respond to the problem the helper has shared with him.

Helper self-disclosure can also undermine helping goals if it makes light of or belittles a client's problem:

'I had a similar experience once but it wasn't really a problem.'

'That's just how I felt when I lost my job. Don't worry, you'll feel better soon.'

Exercise 8.3 invites you to reflect on your experience as a receiver and provider of helper self-disclosure.

EXERCISE 8.3: SELF-DISCLOSURE

1 Think of at least two occasions when others have tried to help you by sharing their own experiences with you.
Was this self-disclosure always helpful?
If not, was it because of any of the following reasons:

■ Too much self-disclosure
■ Irrelevant to my problem
■ Too distracting
■ Made me feel inadequate or anxious
■ Undermined my confidence in the helper
■ Too embarrassing/intimate
■ Other (specify)

Are you able to specify in more detail what it was that the helper actually did that was not helpful?

2 If the helper self-disclosure was *helpful* was it because of one or more of the following reasons:

■ Offered new perspective on my problem
■ Made it easier to talk about my problem
■ Increased my confidence in the helper
■ Other (specify)

Are you able to specify in more detail what it was that the helper actually did that was helpful?

3 Next time you share your own experience with a client open a 'second channel' and monitor your own behaviour. How does your self-disclosing behaviour compare with that which you found helpful? Are you able to identify possibilities for improving the effectiveness of your self-disclosing?

Exercises 8.1, 8.2 and 8.3 have been concerned with improving the quality of the feedback, challenges and self-disclosure offered by the helper. Exercise 8.4 is concerned with quantity rather more than with quality. It examines how often a helper solicits or provides information and considers whether the balance is appropriate relative to the needs of the client.

EXERCISE 8.4: SOLICITING AND PROVIDING INFORMATION

Think of some recent occasions when you occupied the helper role and consider the following questions.

Soliciting information

1   How often did you check with the client whether you had understood what he had said?
2   How often did you consciously pay attention to the verbal and non-verbal cues that provided an indication of how the client was responding to your interventions?
3   How often did you actually solicit feedback from the client about how helpful your interventions had been?

The scale on Figure 8.8 runs from *insufficient* to *optimum level* with an additional shaded zone indicating over-use, ending at *excessive*.

It may be that you paid more attention to some of these behaviours than others but make an overall assessment of how appropriate the level of your 'soliciting behaviour' was. Draw a vertical line to the bottom of your window from the appropriate point on the scale across the top of Figure 8.8.

Providing information

Reflect on those occasions when you offered help and consider, ideally, how much feedback you should have given and how often you should have challenged the client or shared your own experience with him. Using this as a bench-mark now consider:

1   How often you *actually* provided feedback
2   How often you *actually* challenged the client's thinking
3   How often you *actually* shared your own experience with the client.

continued

Locate an overall assessment of the extent to which you actually engaged in 'providing information' relative to the client's need for this behaviour on the scale down the left-hand side of the window, and draw a horizontal line across the window from that point.

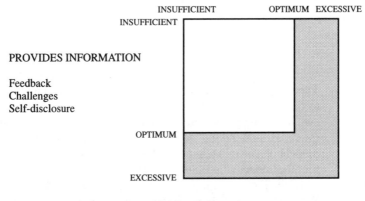

Figure 8.8 Soliciting and providing information

REVIEW QUESTIONS

1 What is the shape of your window? Which of the four helper types presented in Figure 8.7 is most like you?
2 Do you need to reconsider the extent to which you use some of these helping behaviours? If so, what do you need to do more of or less of?

9 *Encouraging creative thinking*

This chapter is concerned with what the helper can do to help others to be more creative. It is primarily concerned with what the helper can do to help the clients in the third (goal setting) and fourth (planning and taking action) stages of the problem management model presented in Chapter 3, but it will also have some implications for other stages of problem management.

Herb Shepard, in the early 1960s, developed a Life Planning Workshop in which participants were invited to write their own obituary. They were asked to think about what they would like others to say about them after they had died. Many people found this a salutary and creative experience in that it helped them to reflect about what was really important and what they really wanted to do with their life. It not only focused their attention on goals but also gave them a different perspective on those goals.

Often, when we are thinking about what we want to achieve, it can be difficult to unhook from the immediate day-to-day pressures that determine our priorities. We are driven by what is urgent and we give insufficient attention to what is really important. Think about the people you know who have had a heart attack or some other life-threatening experience. Many report that the experience gave them a new insight into what really mattered. It changed their perspective on life.

This kind of insight not only is important to goal setting and action planning, but also can contribute to an understanding of what it is that is unsatisfactory about the existing situation.

The problem management model presented in Chapter 3 does not necessarily require the helper and client always to progress, in linear fashion, from stage 1 through to stage 6. It can be an iterative process in which the client moves backwards as well as forwards. The example of the life-threatening experience not only can provide a new perspective on appropriate goals (stage 3) but, because it may shed new light on some aspect of the problem, can move the client back to stage 2 for a better-informed exploration of what it is that is unsatisfactory about the existing situation.

WHY CLIENTS NEED TO DEVELOP THEIR OWN GOALS

Being aware of what is important and developing clear goals that reflect these priorities are essential requirements for effective action. Covey offers some interesting observations on this point in *The Seven Habits of Highly Effective People*, and advocates that we 'begin with the end in mind'. For example, if you are in the fortunate position of being able to design and build your own house you are unlikely to begin building until you have a clear idea about the kind of house you want. If you want it to be a family house in which people are able to spend a lot of time together you may decide to design a large kitchen-cum-family room where members of the family can be together while meals are being prepared and clothes are being washed and ironed. To start building without a plan can be expensive because, as your ideas develop and change, you might have to undertake costly re-work. This is not to say that plans cannot be modified or that intuition should never be the basis for action but the development of clear goals, founded on a thorough understanding of the problem, can be an important contributor to effective action.

Covey argues that if people do not develop a sense of self-awareness and use this to identify what is important and what they want to achieve they will, by default, empower other people and external circumstances to shape much of their life. In other words, rather than working proactively towards what is important to them they will react to external pressures in ways that do little to help them manage their problems more effectively.

Exercise 9.1 asks you to think about a problem situation and identify what a more desirable scenario would look like. Complete this exercise before reading on.

EXERCISE 9.1: PART 1, IDENTIFYING REALISTIC GOALS

Read the following case study. Place yourself in the role of one of the two remaining partners and identify a realistic goal that, if achieved, would bring about a more desirable state of affairs for you and your colleague:

You are a partner in what used to be a thriving dental practice that provided work for three partners, three nurses, a receptionist and a dental mechanic. The practice is based in a wholly owned large detached Victorian house which is in a good state of repair and is set in its own grounds with plenty of parking space in the middle of a wealthy middle-class neighbourhood. In the past an optician used to rent a room and share the reception facilities but when he retired seven years ago he sold his goodwill to another optician located nearby and no attempt was ever made to find a new tenant.

Last year one of the partners had a mild heart attack and decided, at very short notice, to retire. You and your colleague considered a number of alternatives before opting to raise the capital to buy out your old partner and appoint an associate dentist in his place.

Arriving at this decision and finding an associate took almost six months and there was also a further four-week delay before the new associate could start work. He has been working with you for almost three months and, under the terms of his employment, you have to decide within the next two weeks whether you are going to employ him on a more permanent basis with a contract that will give him a minimum of four months' notice if you decide to terminate his employment.

Neither you nor your colleague are very satisfied with his performance. He has made a number of clinical decisions that, while technically correct, neither of you agree with. You have also had a lot of complaints from patients about the way he relates with them and you feel that he is not as cost conscious as he should be.

Added to this you have serious financial worries. The long period without a replacement dentist together with the patient dissatisfaction since the new associate started work have accelerated what had been a gradual decline in the numbers of patients 'on the books'. Even with the new associate's contribution, practice income, month on month, is now less than 70 per cent of what it had been twelve months ago and overheads have continued to rise. You also have the additional burden of interest payments on the capital you raised to buy out your old partner.

continued

What would a more desirable scenario look like? When you have decide what your goal should be make a very brief note of it and the thinking that led up to it. You will be asked to refer back to this in part 2 of the exercise, later in this chapter.

REACTIONS TO UNCERTAINTY

Change is often associated with uncertainty, and the client's reaction to this uncertainty may have an important effect on his approach to problem management. If the client is to move to a more desirable state of affairs he needs to be prepared to change, and an essential step in bringing about any change is letting go of the status quo. However, even when the current situation is clearly unsatisfactory, some people may be reluctant to let go because they are not sure what a more desirable scenario would look like. They may fear that they could 'jump out of the frying pan into the fire'. Helping the client to identify a realistic goal that promises some personal benefit can be a tremendous spur to action. It can inspire and motivate the client.

Uncertainty can also heighten the client's anxiety, which in turn may lead him to seek certainty by looking to others for advice and a sense of direction. If the helper responds by prescribing what the client should do, her actions may encourage the client to become more rather than less dependent on the helper and this may do nothing to help him develop the capacity to manage his own problems more effectively.

LOCKING ON TO A SINGLE SOLUTION

Another effect of uncertainty on the client's behaviour may be to motivate him to find a solution, any solution, as quickly as possible. He may lock on to the first solution he comes across because this allows him to throw himself into action. But remember the argument against solution mindedness presented in Chapter 3, where it was suggested that managers should be thinkers first and doers second. Thinking of alternative goals after one has already been identified might seem a waste of time, but it is better to 'waste time' at the thinking stage because mistakes may be much more difficult to rectify later on.

Heirs believes that alternatives are the raw material of good decisions. Ideas have to be over-produced so that they can be tested and the weak and the unworkable can be identified and eliminated. The more alternatives that are generated the more chance there is of finding one that will be appropriate, but Heirs acknowledges that people can find this difficult to accept:

> All their training and instincts suggests that they should concentrate on finding the one right answer and not waste time dreaming of other, alternative answers. For the person who feels comfortable only when moving forward with a clear goal in mind, the business of letting one's thinking or that of one's colleagues drift in an apparently vague and undisciplined fashion can be distinctly disturbing.
>
> (Heirs, *The Professional Decision Thinker*, p. 56)

but he argues that it is important because to every complex question about possible courses of future action there is likely to be a wide variety of answers, none of which will be clearly right or wrong:

> The aim must be to generate the widest range of possible answers, each of which will have its own peculiar advantages and drawbacks. Once that has been done, the field can be narrowed down to find the answer that has most advantages and the fewest drawbacks – the answer that will prove to be less imperfect than all the other answers proposed.
>
> (*The Professional Decision Thinker*, p. 57)

When people lock on to the first solution they reduce the possibility that alternatives will ever be considered, and there is no guarantee that the first solution will be the best. Sometimes it can be beneficial if the helper can slow the client down and persuade him to consider more than one solution or goal before he invests his energy in the development of action plans.

How many solutions did you generate to the problem presented in Exercise 9.1, part 1?

EXERCISE 9.1: PART 2

Refer back to the case study presented in part 1 of this exercise and reflect on the following questions.

■ How many alternatives did you consider before deciding what the dentists' goal should be?

■ Did you lock on to the first viable solution that came to mind or did you develop a number of possibilities?

■ Was it difficult to develop additional goals after you had thought of the first one?

■ If you did think of a number of goals, how different were they from each other?

■ Overall do you feel that your approach to this problem was sufficiently creative?

Helpers can help their clients generate a range of possible alternatives by encouraging them to consider different ways of framing their goals, and by encouraging them to separate the processes of generating and evaluating goals so that creative thinking is not unnecessarily constrained.

BRAINSTORMING

Creative thinking about goals and about plans to achieve these goals can be facilitated by a technique known as brainstorming. This technique or procedure is based on two principles. The first is that most problems have more than one solution and, therefore, every effort should be made to generate as many alternative solutions as possible. The second is that the process of generating solutions can and should be separated from the process of evaluating solutions in order to free people, during the solution *generation* phase, to be as creative as possible. If this distinction is not made there may be a tendency for people to censor their ideas and think only of 'sensible' or 'workable' solutions. The wild and unconventional ideas that may be suppressed could, if they were available for closer analysis, offer the best way forward or could trigger trains of thought that might lead to other effective solutions.

Brainstorming offers a number of guidelines for injecting more creativity into the process of generating ideas:

1   Generate as many ideas as possible.
2   Avoid self-censorship.
3   Piggyback or build on previous ideas to generate new ones.
4   Do not begin to evaluate any of the ideas until a wide range of alternatives has been generated.

Brainstorming is most commonly used in a group setting but it can be used by people working on their own. When it is used in a group setting one member normally assumes the role of recorder and writes down on a whiteboard or large sheet of paper all the ideas as they are generated by the group. Often this idea-generation session is conducted against the clock, thus increasing the pressure and pace. The final step involves looking for ways of combining or modifying ideas. Usually most people enjoy brainstorming and leave the session feeling that the group has generated ideas that might not otherwise have been considered. There is, however, evidence that the synergy that is generated by people working together is not essential for the generation of a wide range of ideas. Individuals, working on their own, can generate as many ideas as a brainstorming group. The problem is that normally they do not do so even though they are capable of doing it.

This is where the helper can intervene to prompt the client to avoid self-censorship and locking on to the first goal he thinks of. She might simply suggest that it would be helpful to think of alternatives, or she might try to motivate him by challenging him to come up with a target number of ideas within a specified time (for example, at least three more ideas within the next three minutes).

EXERCISE 9.1: PART 3

> Find a scrap pad to make notes, re-read the case presented in part 1 of this exercise and, following the guidelines for brainstorming outlined above, see how many more desirable scenarios or goals you can generate in three minutes.
>
> ~~~~~~~~~~~~~~~~~~~~~~~~
>
> Now look at the ideas you have generated and group similar ideas together. Modify any ideas that you feel will benefit from further refinement. This might involve applying some aspect of one idea to another to produce a meaningful goal from something that might have (at first) appeared 'half baked'.
>
> ~~~~~~~~~~~~~~~~~~~~~~~~
>
> How many ideas did you manage to generate using this procedure? Were you able to think of ideas that did not occur to you the first time round?

Most people find that by adopting this kind of approach they can generate many more ideas than they normally do. This is because the brainstorming procedure encourages them to adopt a divergent approach to thinking which assumes there will be more than one goal. The guidelines prompt them to search for alternatives and caution them against self-censorship. Brainstorming encourages most people to break their habitual approach to thinking, and does so in ways that make it less likely that alternative ideas will be locked out. However, not all of the ideas generated will be realistic and achievable goals.

Once the client has generated a range of possible goals he has to decide which has the most advantages and the fewest disadvantages. One procedure that the helper can use to assist the client decide which goal to adopt is to ask him to select any two goals and explain why he would prefer one rather than the other. If he does this several times he will produce a list of constructs that will point to the criteria he feels must be satisfied by a goal if it is to be acceptable. He can then test each of the goals he has brainstormed against this specification. One fairly formalised way of doing this is to list the criteria down one side of a matrix and the goals across the top, as in

Criteria \ Solutions	1	2	3	4	5
Cost					
Effect on subordinates' satisfaction					
Effect on my satisfaction					
Effect on subordinates' workload					
Effect on my workload					
Total					

Figure 9.1   Goal evaluation matrix

Figure 9.1. This provides a framework within which each goal can be scored against each criterion on a ten-point scale (where 0 = totally fails to satisfy the criterion and 10 = fully satisfies the criterion). The scores for each goal can then be tallied to provide a first guide to which goal might be most satisfactory. Another less cumbersome way is simply to use the criteria as a framework for thinking about, or discussing with the helper, the relative merits of each goal without resorting to any formal scoring procedure.

It was mentioned above that this kind of analysis may provide only a first guide to which goal might be most satisfactory. Once a goal has been identified the helper may, by challenging the client's chosen goal, encourage the client to re-examine whether the criteria he used were adequate. She might do this by asking questions such as:

1   Is this goal your ultimate objective (is it an end in itself) or is it merely a means to some other, more important end?
2   Do you really need to reach this goal in order to improve your state of affairs?
3   What will have changed if you achieve this goal?
4   What will still be the same when you have achieved this goal that might make you less than totally satisfied with the new situation?

Answers to these questions might help the client refine his notion of a more desirable scenario and the criteria of an acceptable goal.

Often clients set themselves 'intermediate goals' that are really a means to some other end and they may never have given much serious consideration to what their ultimate objective is. The helper can assist the client to avoid accepting the first goal he thinks of and can help him to think more clearly about what it is he really wants to achieve.

What do you think the ultimate goal of the dentists might have been in Exercise 9.1? Could it have been to:

- to improve the performance of their new associate;
- to protect the reputation of the practice in the local community;
- to run their practice in a way that restores their income to what it had been twelve months earlier;
- to maximise their income, using their assets in whatever way will enable them to do this, even if it means leaving dentistry and radically changing the nature of their business; or
- to achieve some other objective?

This chapter has considered what the helper can do to help the client think more creatively about his problem. Brainstorming has been introduced as a useful technique but it is not the only way in which the helper can encourage the client to be more creative. She can encourage him to think about things differently by asking him to write his own obituary (as in the Life Planning Exercise mentioned at the beginning of this chapter) or to describe his ideal job or some other ideal scenario. She can ask him to think about what it was like in the past (before the problem arose) and use this image as a basis for generating ideas about how the current situation might be improved. She can use techniques to promote creative thinking such as random word stimulation, where the client is given a word chosen at random and asked to find a link between it and a desirable solution to his problem. She can also ask the client to think about possible analogies for his problem ('it's like being lost in a jungle or standing in the middle of a tinder-dry forest that could burst into flames at any minute'), and ask the him to develop these analogies to find solutions ('I could find a river and swim down it to safety') and consider whether these solutions can suggest possible ways in which the real problem could be managed more effectively.

The technique, be it brainstorming or some other approach to encouraging creative thinking, is only the means to an end, and in this context the end is to help the client to challenge the obvious and to explore alternatives in order to identify and achieve desirable and realistic goals. Helping the client learn how to identify the best alternative before rushing into action can be a very effective way of helping him to help himself.

10 A force-field approach to developing action plans

Helping clients act can be vitally important. After seeing himself on a training video James decided he needed to lose at least thirty pounds but, three months later, when he went for his annual health check, he was alarmed to discover that he had actually gained an extra four pounds and that his weight was a health risk. His lack of success in losing weight might have been attributed to several factors:

1   His goal had not been expressed in terms of specific behaviours, such as exercising more or eating less.
2   He had failed to think through what losing weight required in terms of personal commitment and what factors might affect his level of commitment.
3   He had failed to develop a detailed plan of how he was going to accomplish his goal.

It was noted in Chapter 3 that Lewin viewed the level of behaviour in any situation as the result of a force field comprising a balance of the forces pushing for change (for some different level of behaviour) and forces resisting that change. When the forces pushing in one direction exceed the forces pushing in the opposite direction the dynamic equilibrium changes. The level of behaviour can be changed by adding forces for change in the desired direction (increasing the driving forces) or by diminishing the restraining forces (Figure 10.1).

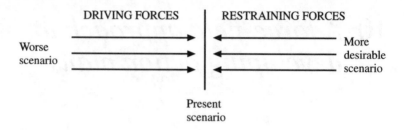

Figure 10.1   A force field

Defining goals in terms of specific behaviours

It can be helpful to think about managing problems more effectively in terms of trying to change processes rather than end states. For example, in the case of James, rather than stating the goal in terms of being thirty pounds lighter it might be more useful if he were to think in terms of the new behaviours that may be required if he is to achieve this state. James might define his goal in terms of eating behaviour. He might decide to eat less than 1200 calories a day (compared with his current consumption of 1900).

Paying attention to motivation and commitment

After giving the matter careful consideration James may have concluded that his current level of consumption (1900 calories) is the result of a set of driving and restraining forces. Some of the restraining forces may be internal to him. For example, because he always feels hungry he finds it very difficult not to eat between meals. If he wants to eat less he will have to decide whether he has the motivation to overcome his hunger pangs. Other restraining forces might be external. His house-bound wife might express her affection for him by investing a lot of her time in the preparation of elaborate meals, and James may feel compelled to eat them in order to avoid hurting her feelings. It is possible that he might be able to think of ways of minimising this problem, but if not he will have to consider whether his motivation to eat less is strong enough to overcome his desire not to hurt his wife's feelings. Both of these are examples of restraining forces that hinder the achievement of his goal. A driving force pushing him in the direction of the preferred scenario might be his desire to lose enough weight to be able to wear his old dinner suit at a works function in order to avoid having to buy a new one. If a new one is very expensive and James is short of cash he might be highly motivated to wear his old one. If, however, his old one is rather old-fashioned he may feel that he should buy a new one even though he is a bit hard up at the moment. In this case his motivation to eat less in order to be able to wear his old suit may be fairly weak.

Developing a detailed action plan

The force-field approach fits well with the six-stage model of helping and the approach to problem management presented in Chapter 3. When the client has identified and clarified his problem and determined what a more desirable scenario would look like he can specify the goal he wants to achieve. This goal provides the basis for a force-field analysis. The client can be helped to list all the restraining forces that are keeping him from his goal and all the driving forces that are helping him reach his goal. At this stage he should be encouraged to list as many as possible and to make no attempt to list them in order of importance.

The next step involves the client reviewing these two lists and identifying those forces which seem to be the most important and which he might also be able to do something about. This latter point relates to the issues of helplessness and locus of control discussed in Chapter 2. Empowering clients might involve the helper working to reverse the expectation that taking action to improve the situation will be a waste of time. However, there may be some forces which are totally beyond the control of the client and both he and helper need to recognise this and not waste too much time and energy on them. Covey, in *The Seven Habits of Highly Effective People*, suggests that there are three types of problem. The first two types are those over which we can exercise direct control by changing our own behaviour and those over which we can exercise only indirect control because we have to change the way somebody else behaves. We might achieve this by changing the way we attempt to influence others. The third type of problem is those over which we have no control. But at least we can manage the way we respond to this type of problem. Egan also addresses this point in *The Skilled Helper*. He distinguishes between influencing realities and accommodating to them and bases his discussion around Weisz *et al.*'s concepts of primary and secondary control, put forward in an article in *American Psychologist*. Clients can exercise primary control by influencing existing realities such as people and situations, and they can exercise

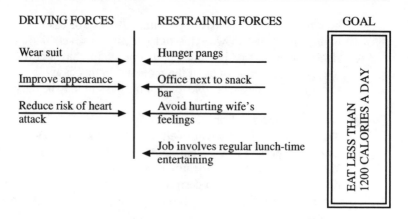

Figure 10.2   James's force field

secondary control by accommodating to realities and maximising satisfaction and goodness of fit with things as they are. Egan describes helping as the art of the possible. While most clients can exercise more primary control over their lives than they actually do, secondary control might be the only realistic option for some.

When the key forces have been identified the client can review each one in more detail. For each key restraining force he might think about all the possible action steps which he could take to reduce the effect of the force. Similarly for each key driving force he might think about all the possible action steps which could increase the effect of the force. At this stage it can be useful to list as many action steps as possible without worrying too much about how practical or effective they would be. The aim should be to be as creative as possible. Brainstorming can play a useful role here.

Having generated a wide range of ideas the client then needs to go over them again to identify those which seem most promising, bearing in mind such practical considerations as the availability of people, time and other resources. It is very important at this stage that the helper does not impose her own values. The client's commitment to the action plan is crucial and therefore he must select action steps that are in keeping with his own values.

The final phase involves reviewing the chosen action steps from the point of view of how they might be brought together to fit into a comprehensive and workable action plan. It may be necessary to modify or eliminate items which do not fit in with the overall plans. It might also be necessary to add new steps which will round out the plan.

Exercise 10.1 invites you to test this approach on a problem that you are faced with. In the example given above James was able define his goal in concrete behavioural terms. He wanted to eat less than 1200 calories a day. He was also able to identify some of the driving and restraining forces that were influencing his behaviour. This information is presented in Figure 10.2.

EXERCISE 10.1: FORCE FIELD ANALYSIS

1   Think about your problem in terms of what is wrong with the existing situation and what a more desirable scenario would look like, and identify a concrete and achievable goal you wish to achieve. Write this goal in the box down the right-hand side of the page.

2   Down the left-hand side of the page list the driving forces that are pushing towards the more desirable scenario and down the right-hand side list the restraining forces which are blocking the achievement of your goal.

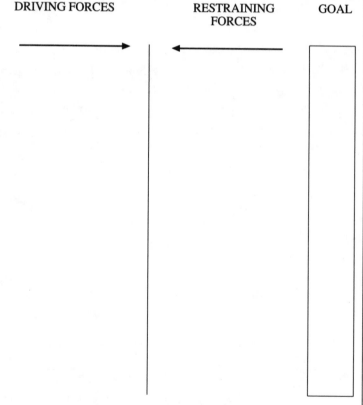

DRIVING FORCES   RESTRAINING   GOAL
                              FORCES

Review your list of driving and restraining forces and place an asterisk beside those which you think are most important *and* that you might be able to do something about. Now rank-order them in terms of their likely contribution to the achievement of your goal.

Review each of the driving forces you marked with an asterisk (starting with the most important) and brainstorm all the steps you could take to increase the effect of the force. Do not confine yourself to 'sensible' ideas. List everything that comes to mind.

DRIVING
FORCE ....
Brainstorm action steps to increase the effect of this force.

DRIVING
FORCE ....
Brainstorm action steps to increase the effect of this force.

DRIVING
FORCE ....
Brainstorm action steps to increase the effect of this force.

DRIVING
FORCE ....
Brainstorm action steps to increase the effect of this force.

DRIVING
FORCE . . . .
Brainstorm action steps to increase the effect of this force.

DRIVING
FORCE . . . .
Brainstorm action steps to increase the effect of this force.

DRIVING
FORCE . . . .
Brainstorm action steps to increase the effect of this force.

DRIVING
FORCE . . . .
Brainstorm action steps to increase the effect of this force.

Do not evaluate any of these action steps until you have brainstormed
action steps to reduce the effect of the restraining forces.

Now do the same for the most important restraining forces, but this time brainstorm all the steps you could take *to reduce* the effect of each restraining force.

RESTRAINING
FORCE ....
Brainstorm the steps you could take to *reduce* the effect of this force.

RESTRAINING
FORCE ....
Brainstorm the steps you could take to *reduce* the effect of this force.

RESTRAINING
FORCE ....
Brainstorm the steps you could take to *reduce* the effect of this force.

RESTRAINING
FORCE ....
Brainstorm the steps you could take to *reduce* the effect of this force.

RESTRAINING
FORCE . . . .
Brainstorm the steps you could take to *reduce* the effect of this force.

RESTRAINING
FORCE . . . .
Brainstorm the steps you could take to *reduce* the effect of this force.

RESTRAINING
FORCE. . . . .
Brainstorm the steps you could take to *reduce* the effect of this force.

RESTRAINING
FORCE
Brainstorm the steps you could take to *reduce* the effect of this force.

Now review all the action steps:

1 Eliminate those that are totally impractical (but only after you are sure that they cannot be 'twisted' or adapted to provide a useful contribution).

2 Identify the 'best of the rest'. Consider whether some action steps can contribute to the strengthening of more than one driving force or the erosion of more than one restraining force. A similar approach to distilling out the most useful action steps is to group similar action steps together and identify those from each group that seem most practical.

3 Finally, list those action steps that deserve serious consideration below.

ACTION TO INCREASE DRIVING FORCES	ACTION TO DIMINISH RESTRAINING FORCES	GOAL

The final step involves re-evaluating the action steps from a cost–benefit perspective. The plan has to be practical and some of the proposed action steps might be too expensive in terms of time or other resources. It may be necessary to amend the plan at this stage in order to improve its viability. However, it may also be necessary to include new elements to mould the individual action steps into an integrated plan. Also give some thought to time scale and milestones against which progress can be assessed. Milestones are important because they can provide early warning if the plan is not working and can signal the need for renewed effort or the implementation of a contingency plan.

Did this force-field exercise help you to think about your problem in a more ordered way? Most people find it provides them with a useful framework, although some do find that it is not always easy to identify the driving and restraining forces that apply to their problem situation. A useful starting point can be to ask the client to consider what it is that is stopping him achieving his goal (the restraining forces) and then move on to talk about what he and others are doing (or could do) to help achieve the goal (driving forces), and for the helper to start to organise the answers within the framework of a force-field chart. The client can then be invited to continue with the analysis in terms of driving and restraining forces. This will usually lead into a discussion of what action the client could take to weaken the restraining and strengthen the driving forces.

One of the most useful benefits of the force-field approach is that it focuses the client's attention on the possibility of reducing the effect of restraining forces. An action plan that is concerned only with increasing the effect of driving forces may be less effective (because of the tension and conflict it may produce) than one that attends to, or even concentrates on, reducing the effect of restraining forces. If the restraining forces are weakened the balance of the remaining forces will push the situation towards the desired scenario.

11 *Knowing when to withdraw*

At the end of Chapter 2 it was stated that the aim of helping was to encourage and assist others to become more proactive in the management of their own problems, to help them to help themselves. In practice this involves helping clients apply a problem management approach to their current situation and, through this experience, develop a more effective approach to problem management which they can apply in a variety of situations. In other words, helping others to help themselves involves helping them develop transferable skills.

DEVELOPING SELF-EFFICACY

Offering help does not involve taking over somebody's problem and solving it for him. It involves empowering the client to manage his own problems more effectively. In many situations the helper might feel more competent than the client to manage the immediate problem situation but the helper must be careful not to take charge. Her aim is to help the client manage the problem for himself, to make him more independent rather than to make him more dependent on her help. This involves respecting the client's right to determine his own fate and to make 'mistakes'. If the helper never allows the client the freedom and autonomy to make mistakes and always intervenes to make sure that every detail of the problem is managed effectively she may deny him the opportunity to learn from his experience. This is a common problem where the helper is a manager and the client is her subordinate. If the manager remains too controlling and fails to modify her relationship with her subordinate in a way that gradually provides him with less help then the manager may fail to help her subordinate develop his full potential.

From the very beginning of the helping relationship the helper needs to be thinking of withdrawing her help and leaving her client to get on with his life. The aim of the effective helper is to make herself redundant as soon as possible.

DECIDING WHEN TO WITHDRAW

The most appropriate time to withdraw will depend on the client. All that some clients may need is a little help to develop a more objective view of their problem. Others may require help to identify realistic goals, but once they have a clear objective to work towards they may be perfectly capable of managing their problem for themselves. However, some clients might require help with every stage of problem management, and some may even need help with more than one problem before it is possible to change their belief that they are unable to help themselves.

It is not unusual for the client to recognise that it is time to terminate the helping relationship before the helper is prepared to accept that the client is ready to 'go it alone'. The helper may be slow to recognise that her withdrawal may be appropriate for any of a number of reasons. It may be that she suspects that the client is reluctant to continue the helping relationship because he wants to escape from a relationship that he finds too disturbing or too challenging and would rather be left to go about things in his own (comfortable) way. For example, the helper may feel that she has worked hard to help the client develop a better understanding of the problem only to find that he seems ready to accept a less than satisfactory situation rather than try to change it. Alternatively the helper may be slow to recognise the time to withdraw because, although she feels the client has made good progress, she may feel that he has more to learn about problem management and that he still needs supporting for a little while longer, even though he may feel ready to tackle the next step or a new problem on his own.

Some helpers have unrealistically high expectations about what it is possible to achieve through the helping relationship and are reluctant to end it until these expectations have been satisfied. In *Guiding Therapeutic Change*, Kanfer and Schefft point to a dilemma that confronts most helpers at some time. They know that the generalisation of new behaviour patterns into everyday life can take considerable time but they are also aware that this time and other resources may not always be available. Consequently the helper has to limit her interventions and accept the inevitability of termination, even when she has clients who have made good progress but who remain short of perfection.

It can also be difficult for the helper to let go if she fails to appreciate just how much progress the client has made. In the first example above, the helper's disappointment with the client's wish to draw the helping relationship to a close may have been because she felt that the client had been overwhelmed by the complexity of the problem and had responded in a way that would not improve his ability to manage other problems in the future. However, from the client's point of view, the decision to accept the situation may have reflected a mature approach to problem management. He may have reached this decision after screening his problems to determine whether they deserve further attention. After careful consideration, he may have decided that the cost of trying to change the situation would far outweigh any benefits. Screening is a valuable problem management skill that can be applied in a variety of situations.

DECIDING HOW TO WITHDRAW

The helper's assessment that accepting the situation would leave the client in an unsatisfactory situation may have been just that, the helper's assessment. Empathising with the client is important throughout the helping process and can minimise the likelihood that helper and client will make different assessments about progress. It can be useful to include a review of what the client has learned as part of almost every interaction between helper and client. Not only can it promote the development of transferable problem management skills but it can also improve the helper's awareness of the client's progress and can make it easier to identify the most appropriate time to withdraw.

In those situations where the client has become dependent on the helper it might be more difficult for the helper to terminate the relationship. One way of drawing a relationship to a close is to increase the interval between meetings and to shift the emphasis towards helping the client plan what he is going to do and to reviewing how successful this action has been. As the period between meetings increases the client has to assume more responsibility for his actions and to develop his own contingency plans when things do not work out according to plan.

When the helper is a manager and the client is a subordinate or a colleague the occupants of these roles may well have been interacting on a regular basis long before the start of the helping relationship and they may well continue to relate after the need for help has been satisfied. In this kind of situation withdrawal can be more problematic than where the helping relationship involves a counsellor and a client who meet only to deal with a specific problem. In this kind of helping relationship it can be relatively easy for the counsellor to withdraw whereas in the former situation withdrawal involves changing the nature of (rather than ending) the relationship. Managing this change may require considerable self-discipline on the part of the manager if the client is to be allowed the space to try things out for himself and to learn from his mistakes. It may also be difficult for the helper/manager to contain her curiosity and to resist the temptation to constantly enquire how well the (former) client is managing. However, in spite of these difficulties, the helper needs to manage an appropriate withdrawal if the help she offers is to help others to help themselves.

Further reading

Bolton, R. (1986) *People Skills*, Sydney: Prentice-Hall of Australia. A well organised and very readable communication skills handbook written for practitioners.

Covey, S.R. (1989) *The Seven Habits of Highly Effective People*, London: Simon and Schuster. A best-selling book which offers an integrated, principle-centred approach for managing personal and professional problems.

Egan, G. (1975, 1982, 1986, 1990) *The Skilled Helper*, Belmont, Calif.: Wadsworth. A widely used text for helpers working with all kinds of clients. It presents a three-stage helping model that provides guiding principles rather than simplistic formulae. The earlier editions of the book focus more on helping the client understand the problem situation, but in later editions greater attention is giver to helping the client act to manage problems more effectively. This book is highly recommended for those who wish to learn more about the principles of helping.

Hayes, J. (1991) *Interpersonal Skills: Goal Directed Behaviour at Work*, London: Routledge. A text which develops many of the ideas discussed in this book and provides more detailed references for those who would like to investigate the relevant literature.

Morris, D. (1977) *Manwatching: A Field Guide to Human Behaviour*, London: Jonathan Cape. A very readable book, written in a popular style, which offers many interesting insights into non-verbal behaviour.

References

Argyris, C. (1982) The executive mind and double-loop learning, *Organizational Dynamics*, Autumn, 5–22.

Blake, R.R. and Mouton, J.S. (1986) *Consultation: A Handbook for Individual and Organization Development*, Reading, Mass.: Addison-Wesley.

Bolton, R. (1986) *People Skills*, Sydney: Prentice-Hall.

Carkhuff, R.R. (1973) *The Art of Helping: An Introduction to Life Skills*, Amherst, Mass.: Human Resource Development Press.

Covey, S.R. (1989) *The Seven Habits of Highly Effective People*, London: Simon and Schuster.

de Bono, E. (1991) *I Am Right – You Are Wrong*, Harmondsworth: Penguin.

Deetz, S.A. and Stevenson, S.L. (1986) *Managing Interpersonal Communication*, New York: Harper and Row.

Driscoll, R. (1984) *Pragmatic Psychotherapy*, New York: Van Nostrand Reinhold.

Egan, G. (1975, 1986, 1990) *The Skilled Helper*, Belmont, Calif.: Wadsworth.

Francis, D. (1990) *Effective Problem Solving*, London: Routledge.

Hackney, H. and Cormier, L.S. (1979) *Counselling Strategies and Objectives*, 2nd edition, Englewood Cliffs, N.J.: Prentice-Hall.

Hargie, O., Saunders, C. and Dickson, D. (1987) *Social Skills in Interpersonal Communication*, 2nd edition, London: Croom Helm.

Hayes, J. (1991) *Interpersonal Skills: Goal Directed Behaviour at Work*, London: Routledge.

Heirs, B. (1986) *The Professional Decision Thinker*, London: Sidgwick and Jackson.

Jackson, K.F. (1977) *The Art of Problem Solving*, London: Hodder and Stoughton.

Jourard, S.M. (1971) *The Transparent Self*, New York: Van Nostrand Reinhold.

Kanfer, F.H. and Schefft, B.K. (1988) *Guiding Therapeutic Change*, Champaign, Ill.: Research Press.

Kotter, J.P. and Schlesinger, L.A. (1979) Choosing strategies for change,

Harvard Business Review, 57, 106–14.

Lewin, K. (1947) Frontiers in group dynamics, *Human Relations*, 1, 5–41.

Lippitt, R., Watson, J. and Westley, B. (1958) *The Dynamics of Planned Change*, New York: Harcourt Brace Jovanovich.

Locke, E.A. and Latham, G.P. (1984) *Goal Setting: A Motivational Technique That Works*, Englewood Cliffs, N.J.: Prentice-Hall.

McGregor, D. (1961) *The Human Side of Enterprise*, New York: McGraw-Hill.

May, R. (1969) *Love and Will*, New York: W.W. Norton.

Morris, D. (1977) *Manwatching: A Field Guide to Human Behaviour*, London: Jonathan Cape.

Phares, E.J. (1976) *Locus of Control in Personality*, Morristown, N.J.: General Learning Press.

Reddy, M. (1987) *The Manager's Guide to Counselling at Work*, London: British Psychological Society/Methuen.

Rogers, C.R. (1951) *Client Centered Therapy*, Boston: Houghton Mifflin.

Rotter, J.R. (1971) External control and internal control, *Psychology Today*, June, 37.

Seligman, M.E.P. (1975) *Helplessness*, San Francisco: W.H. Freeman.

Weisz, J.R., Routhbaum, F.M. and Blackburn, T.C. (1984) Standing out and standing in: the psychology of control in America and Japan, *American Psychologist*, 39, 955–69.